∞ *The* Journe *of* ∞ *Mortimer* *Fish*

By
Tim Stafford

Illustrations
Pippa Unwin

The Journal of Mortimer Fish

The Adventures and Mishaps
of a Jack Russell terrier.
As told in her own words
to Him.

A Dolphin Publications Book

First published in Great Britain in 2003

ISBN 0-9545738-0-3

Published by
Dolphin Publications
20 Chettle
Blandford,
Dorset, DT11 8DB
email: durhamtim@hotmail.com
Tel: 01258 830429

Printed and bound by The Baskerville Press Ltd.
Salisbury, Wiltshire

Dedication

To Him, His relatives and friends who have had to suffer all
the slings and arrows (not to mention teeth)
of the last two years.

Thanks are very much due to:

Sandra Pope who had the hideous task of unravelling
the scribbling that He calls handwriting.

The Lovely Kate for keeping Him sane some of the time and
looking after me when He went away.

Heather who still looks harassed at the state of His house and who,
we think, has never quite recovered from
the episode of the balls in a jar.

Bodgit who in association with Him has done
stirling work keeping the profits good at
various distilleries in Scotland.

And finally to David Burnett of the Dovecote Press
who has been such a help to Him
without a single fee note.

Apologies

To the raft of publishers who have been bombarded with scruffy
typescripts and who then had to send them all home again with very
nice letters (all of them liked the drawings by Pippa Unwin).

N.B.

Should anyone want to sue Him don't bother.
He's spent it all on whisky, horses and helicopters.

Foreword

TO THE JOURNAL OF MORTIMER FISH

" I really don't understand why you have to chew everything!" He said soon after I had moved in with Him. My response was simple "Had He ever tried?" This rather threw Him and illustrates how perhaps we got off on the wrong foot and how things could only get better.

I admit that being away from parental control for the first time in the eight weeks of my life made me a little inclined to run wild but in retrospect perhaps I did give Him quite a hard time.

First of all there were these two old dogs who were in the house when I got there. They were by any standards not very welcoming and growled a good deal and even snapped now and then when I playfully nipped one of them in her skirts. Still, I do not think that the language they used was necessary. There was this really bad tempered Collie who I call "Bugger Off" for no better reason that they were the only words that invariably fitted the bill whenever she hove into view. Then there was the pretty ancient Labrador who spent more or less her entire life asleep except when a meal was in the offing at which point she sort of lit up. I call her " Comatose". In the kitchen Percy the Parrot lives in a cage on a table. He does absolutely nothing most of the time but now and then sets up a fearful screeching noise. I'd cook him if I were Him.

Outside the house were some curious looking Bantam hens which I initially regarded as live targets until He put me right on that subject and some ordinary chickens in a run. The evil tempered cat "Blot" is hardly worth mentioning really. I had my Brother Piglet who is owned by The Lovely Kate to play with every day. He was fat and idle but better than nothing I suppose.

His housekeeper, Heather, relentlessly tried to keep abreast of His domestic needs. It was a daunting task which she tackled valiantly. Most of the time she smiled bravely while navigating the Dyson round the chaos.

The stable yard seemed to be bursting at the seams with those great brutes He took hunting a couple of days a week and this is where His groom The Lovely Kate spent most of her time though, as will be seen, she somehow found her way into the domestic quarters in time.

He tried very hard to potty train me but logic dictated that if the horses were allowed to do it in their bedrooms why couldn't I? I dug loads of holes all over His garden looking for subterranean foes. He filled them in and then dug His own and planted things in them. Madness!

I also had to come to terms with His hobbies which ranged from the mundane of gardening through the predictable hunting and fishing to the frankly bizarre of flying a small and noisy helicopter all of which took up so much of His daylight hours that it was not surprising that He didn't seem to have much time for earning a living.

Having been widowed He inevitably hadn't entirely given up all hope of a renewed romantic life one day and His attempts in this direction caused us all a lot of amusement. There seemed to be a more or less seamless procession of possible girl friends but perhaps His most fanciful passion centred on His young and glamorous groom The Lovely Kate. It was she who presented me to Him as occupational therapy. It must have worked because His hair has gone a lovely shade of grey and lots of it has fallen out since I got here. I expect that those are good signs.

And so, because my life became somewhat surreal in the sense that every day was something of an adventure for all of us, I thought I should record as much of it as seemed appropriate and repeatable. The following pages tell the tale of my growing pains and beyond, in this odd but essentially happy environment.

The
Journal
of
Mortimer Fish - A Terrier

19th April

I have been billeted on this old chap today which is, apparently, the anniversary of His Father's death not so long ago and by the look of Him He won't be far behind. He's a bit dithery and rather forgetful and lives in a rambling farmhouse which is decidedly tatty set in the middle of a village of cottages, houses and a large mansion all owned by the same family headed up by His friend Bodgit who lives in the really big house. There are only about eighty people in the village none of whom seem to have any regular work. Some of the houses are pretty thatched cottages and some aren't. I like the sound of the thatched ones as I rather think that they might yield the odd rat. His isn't pretty or thatched but it has a big walled garden which seems to open up all sorts of opportunities from my stand point (which isn't very high yet!) There are two other dogs. A very dozy (she's nearly always asleep when she's not eating) Labrador called "Comatose" and a border collie called "Bugger Off". They made some very discouraging noises when I arrived. That won't do at all. They are both pretty crabby and almost dead so it won't be long before I'll be in charge.

He's mad keen on his garden but you couldn't tell from the state of it. At the weekend He planted, in a terracotta pot near the house, some rather common night scented stock which I don't like the look of at all, so I dealt with those in no time at all - they won't give any trouble now - wherever they are. He spent the whole weekend mowing, weeding and fiddling about with the flower borders almost without a break and then complained that He was tired. I can't see the point. Nothing in it seems edible or chaseable so why work yourself into a lather about it all.

20th April

My brother, Piglet, is owned by the Lovely Kate, who is His groom. They turned up today. She is tall and slim with long blonde hair and pretty, but young enough to be His Granddaughter. However try telling Him that. The steam coming out of His ears is almost visible. It turns out that Kate knows my Mother and that is why I'm here. Kate calls me His "occupational therapy". I'm not sure that I know what that means but I think it has something to do with Him being rather suddenly on His own. Piglet is big, fat and soft. I chased him round the garden a few times and he took refuge behind some more terracotta pots which I hadn't noticed. Quite nice if you like that sort of thing. I think they need more careful inspection once I've dealt with my brother. I bet they are full of really dumb plants which should be redistributed round the garden or onto the compost heap in due course. I doubt if He would notice.

There are very long flower borders running most of the length of the walled garden. One is full of boring old plants and is backed by a high brick wall. Piglet and me are thinking of making an escape route along the base of this wall. It looks quite promising. I don't suppose He will notice. At the far end is a vegetable garden with chestnut paling fencing and hedges all round it. One has to suppose that these barricades are to prevent entry by unauthorised people like me, Piglet and co. A bit hopeful if you ask me.

Nigel Dempster came to the village today too. He sailed up to Nigel claiming to have been at school with him, as He put it, "about a million years ago" and by the look of them both that is not such an exaggeration. I will quite surprised if one of them hasn't popped off by lunch time.

26th April

He went fishing today with Comatose, leaving Bugger Off and me here. When He came home grumbling and empty-handed I managed to escape to the sitting room where I put some rabbits to ground in the sofa and then fetched them out again. He wasn't too pleased, so I got under the Chinese cupboard which contains His television and under which He stores His videos and scattered a few of them round the room where they looked quite pleasing. He didn't agree, grumpy old man. The Lovely Kate fed us.

It has to be said that it's quite a good house for a terrier in early life because it is arranged in rather a higgledy-piggledy way having been added onto over the centuries so has lots of nooks and crannies. Once it was probably quite smart. Now there is practically no horizontal surface that isn't littered with some wretched ornament or photograph of horses and ageing or dead relatives. Well they look dead or nearly dead to me anyway. One room is floor to ceiling books. It is often rather cobwebby and dusty and the books don't get much exercised by being read. Some of them have delicious smelling leather covers. I will have to investigate those sometime.

Bodgit who is His best buddy in the village came to see Him today to discuss world affairs and to complain about the interfering government. The subject of fox hunting seemed to dominate the conversation. It didn't take too long for the whisky bottle to be brought out and after a time the volume of their discourse increased in direct proportion to the rate of consumption. Then the subject of the stock market came up and a gloom descended. He looked vacantly at the ceiling and Bodgit scratched his grey beard turning the corners in so that he could chew them. Rather a disgusting habit I think. After a bit Bodgit tottered off again and He subsided behind His glass and watched the television in a rather vacant way, mumbling. I think they are both quite odd.

6th May

He takes us all for a walk first thing in the morning into the field at the end of the garden. I think that this uncomfortable expedition is an attempt to get me into the way of doing 'you knows' outside which, if He was intelligent enough, He would realise is just a non-starter. The field is full of long grass (long to me, you understand, my little legs seem ill adapted to the terrain). He says it's for our benefit - He needn't bother so far as I'm concerned. Today we met an elderly village cat which sat on the path and looked disdainfully at me. I didn't like its attitude. I'll deal with it later. Every day a bunch of Guernsey heifers come racing to the fence and make absurd girly mooing noises in what is frankly a pretty aggressive way. I'll deal with them later too. I don't think this village is at all well organised. However I will soon sort that out.

7th May

One of His little diversions is learning to fly a helicopter. God help the world if He succeeds judging by His car driving ability. He took me to the airfield today. It is miles away so during the journey I get to whiz round the car and discover interesting smells in all those disgusting corners He never sees into. What a dismal place the airfield is. An enormous expanse of grass with huge boring buildings here and there, out of which come stupid noisy machines.

He pushed off to see His long suffering instructor so I investigated the shopping from Waitrose which was in the back of the car buried under His fishing gear in a rather pathetic attempt, I suppose, to keep it from prying noses. It proved very dull. The faint smell of chicken drew me but it turned out to be a stock cube. It's astonishing how they can compress a whole bird into such a tiny package. Some of "Them" must be quite bright. After the disappointment of the shopping I got my own back on the way home by behaving incredibly badly in the car. I disappeared behind and under the front passenger seat and made a terrific smell so that He thought that I had done a 'you know' there. He got quite jittery and His driving went even more to pot. Then I lay on the front seat next to Him and fixed Him with my most gimlet eye while in the "pounce" position. This so unnerved Him that His driving got worse. He got flashed at by another driver who assumed that the erratic driving indicated drunkenness. I have since discovered that this isn't as fanciful as it might at first seem. A good journey full of interest. When we got home Piglet came to see me and He rather obviously drooled over Kate. Sad really.

10th May

Today He took me for a walk in the New Forest. The other dogs came too. I don't even like walking. Within yards of the start Bugger Off was chased by a pony with a very young foal. The ground was sodden, and there were endless puddles, streams and bogs and the place was covered in trees, none of which seemed to yield a chaseable creature. All the holes were full of water and the damp in my coat itched. Comatose seemed concerned that resting places seemed rather few and far between. Bugger Off skulked. What a perfectly ghastly place. He got chatted up by some old bint at the reptile centre on the way home. You could see He was a bit chuffed - He was quite nice for a short time. We fell out after supper. I did a 'you-know' in the kitchen and He cracked His hunting whip at me, so I bit it and him. Crabby old man. Rotten day. The only bright bit was Bugger Off being attacked - serves her right, miserable old cow.

15th May

Not such a bad day. He has been in the garden most of the time and I've helped. You would have thought that by His time in life He would be good at digging holes but I think He's incompetent at the job. However, He'll learn under my direction. I've only done one 'you know' in doors - if you ignore the night time. He got a bit ratty about that. I nearly got the Labrador playing but at the last minute her dignity, combined with an attack of tiredness caught up with her and she had to have a little lie down. I managed to chase the bantams now and then but they gave the game away by squawking. He talks big about the hunting whip. It's really good sport but I keep a wary eye open for this whip - who knows, He might mean it.

16th May

He got up looking frankly clapped out and was bad tempered. I hung onto the turn-ups on His trousers a bit and He was not pleased. He tramped round the place in a grumpy sort of way and left as soon as He could. He left me here and went flying His silly little helicopter again. Where's the down-hole excitement in that? He came back in better fettle so He set himself to mowing the lawn in rather untidy lines. Another of His stepchildren arrived and began to witter on at Him. He said that He couldn't cope with being "Jemmered" so often, whatever that means. I think it might have a clue to her name but He is so obscure in some of His terminology. He sent her off to ride the skewbald horse. I'm not sure yet where she fits into the scenario but no doubt all will be revealed in due course. I've been goodish all day – only one 'you know' in the house (that He knows about). He's getting better at the food thing. What on earth He thought He was doing with all that "puppy" stuff I just can't think. Milksops and cardboard. What's wrong with a nice putrid rat or mole?

18th May

He has been quite livable with today even though I did leave one or two 'you knows' over night. He left us until half past seven in the morning so He can't really complain. He went to Waitrose shopping as usual and was away absolutely ages. He came back with the car groaning under the weight of their distinctive plastic bags which He has to hide from the people in the village shop. There was a lot of moaning from Him about the size of the pet food bill. I bet it pales into insignificance compared with His whisky account. He was rather grumpy about my 'you know' in the kitchen. I can't say I was too concerned.

Heather is His housekeeper and surprise, surprise she too is a young blonde. She lives in a neighbouring village and comes here three times a week in a vain attempt to sort out His domestic chaos. Now and then you can see the despair on her face. It seems an endless matter of trundling about behind Him, so to speak, pushing the Dyson. Today she brought her little daughter who played with me which was good sport. Later on Kate turned up looking very summery in shorts, which made Him nearly self-destruct. She took us for a walk during which Bugger Off displayed her evil temper by skulking and snapping indiscriminately and Piglet his enormous bulk. I could swear that Comatose can walk in her sleep.

I did some serious 'you knows' in the garden which sent Him into raptures – it's very odd the things that seem to please Him. He gave me an excellent supper – I wonder where that will end up.

21st May

We (Him and me) fell out early today. I did a 'you know' in the dining room – I admit it was pure laziness and excitement on my part but He was really crabby and hit me on the nose. Sensibly in my opinion I bared my teeth at Him. He missed my nose and caught one of my canines and made a big hole in His hand Ha! Ha! Serve Him right – I slept outside for a bit while He cooled down. After that things got better and better. Piglet came to see me, and He drooled again and went off with Kate for what I imagine was another session of middle-aged angst. Poor old man.

Bodgit came to see Him today. His name apparently has something to do with the work he tries to do. Actually I have yet to see any of them do anything much in the way of gainful employment. Bodgit's mode of transport is a rickety old bicycle which he rides round the village in all weathers in bare feet. He always seems to arrive as the top comes off the whisky bottle. He wandered into the house as if he owned the place, whistling tunelessly, just as I needed to be reminded about 'you knows,' but they were busy putting the world to rights, and so He didn't remind me. The inevitable happened. They really are hopeless when they take their eyes off my ball. Good supper of chicken. I chased a couple of bantams after supper then I went to bed. I am now sleeping with the enemy – the dozy Labrador – what a waffler she is. I can't believe how crabby Bugger Off is either.

25th May

He went fishing again and came back in a bad mood with all sorts of tales of excitement and lost monsters. He did have one quite decent fish with Him so I can't think why He has to be so miserable. I suppose it's His age.

Comatose is really quite decent sometimes. When she thinks no one is watching, she sniffs me affectionately. I notice, of course - not much gets past me – but she tries to make sure no-one else does. Kate took us for a walk. I see what He sees in her, but it demonstrates the pinnacle of hope over reality. Still, I suppose there comes a time in life when dreaming is just about all that's left to the very old. He got round rather a lot of whiskies tonight and went to bed in a fair old state (doors left open, lights on and some falling over upstairs). God knows what He'll be like tomorrow.

28th May

I thought He was quite ungrateful today. I'd gone all through the night, if you see what I mean - and that sort of pleased Him, so I brought Him some presents just to gain even more brownie points - trinkets, such as an old teabag, a snail which was littering the garden, some bits of wood and the real prize; an enormous legless black beetle. He threw them all out of the kitchen window with an ill grace. I'm not sure that I'll bother again.

Incidentally, there are no rabbits in the sofa. I've given it a thorough going over - slight whiff of rat maybe, which gives some indication of the conditions here. No wonder poor Heather sometimes looks so despondent.

31st May

Oh dear! I did all right today but at the moment when I usually get to duff up Piglet on the lawn He tossed us into the kitchen and took the glamorous Kate and delectable Heather off to the aerodrome for a jolly in his silly helicopter. Piglet and I had a fantastic time rioting in the kitchen - unfortunately the excitement got to our inside bits and we did rather flood the place. He turned up noisily with rather green looking women, parking the silly thing at the end of the garden in the field, had a cup of tea and flew off again leaving the sick looking women here. Eventually He returned to cook me a nice supper - rather hot chicken but very nice. I went to bed in Comatose's delicious smelling bed - more of a pit really. It has some pretty vintage smells that have accumulated over the decades I suppose. I must say His lifestyle doesn't look too healthy to me and seems to be pretty boring. The mixture of whisky, women and helicopters would suggest a fairly lethal mixture in someone of such advanced years.

5th June

He says that He is at home this weekend, which gives me a chance to help Him rearrange the garden which He seems to have allowed to get into a fearful muddle. I cannot believe He has ever really understood the significance of holes and their part in a full and active life. I think that He and I have a fundamental and probably irreconcilable disagreement about the function of holes. He digs just about as many as me but, bafflingly, He puts things into them whereas I wait for something chaseable to come out of mine. As yet I haven't seen one of His boring old plants leg it up the garden.

I wonder if anyone has ever noticed what a muddle a canine body is. Good to look at but with sticky-out bits which all need attending to. I say this because at breakfast time I had had a go at the rabbit in my day-bed which is a pleasantly smelly old Puffa coat in front of the Aga. In the course of that enterprise I noticed that something was sticking out at the back so I bit it - rather a mistake really because it was one of my own legs but next to it was another bit which suddenly caught my eye - my tail - and what a worry that is. It has no notion of staying still - try as I might, it keeps moving which, when you've been down a pretend rabbit hole (a disorientating experience anyhow) is a nuisance because I kept falling over - very undignified. As ever He found it all rather amusing and gave me that inane grin which rather unnerves me. Anyhow, to cut a long story short I found other things that stick out and dealt with them too and then settled down to chewing my day-bed which is all the wrong shape.

Incidentally I don't go much on His comment that it is curious that a Dog's smile is located on its bottom. Rather personal in my view and a bit obscure.

6th June

There is a veranda the entire length of the garden side of the house. It is supported on pillars and has a glass roof. When the sun shines the terrace becomes nice and warm and a haven for all sorts of garden dwellers. For instance there is a bees nest under the paving and the bees come and go by means of small holes between the slabs. I bite the bees as they emerge - now and then they bite back. It's only fair I suppose. It just goes to reinforce my view that interesting things emerge from holes but I've never seen anything interesting remain static in one.

It is quite extraordinary, someone put a bicycle in the garden without telling me (or asking). Of course, I didn't know it was a bicycle, I thought it was an alien being and I admit to a moment or two of panic, so I went into the dining room and threatened it through the French windows. Eventually He explained, so I relaxed again but as I have said before if I'm not told about these things how on earth can I develop in the proper way?

9th June

He took me on holiday today. It all started rather badly – I was under the chest in the hall fearing I was in trouble because He kept calling me. He tried to get me out by sugary encouragement which didn't fool me for a moment, so when He put his hand under to grab me I bit Him. After a moment or two discussing this and other seemingly unrelated apparent transgressions, we set off for the South and I slept a good deal on the way. Before settling down I did my usual trick of disappearing behind the seat which got Him a bit rattled – it really is a good ploy. I do enjoy the look of panic on His face.

Anyhow, we were going on a steamer to the Island of Purbeck – so He said, smiling in an indulgent sort of way which made me nearly puke. I looked out of the car while we were at sea and couldn't see any steam, and it has to be said that the sea was very calm and terribly short.

Once we had reached land about five minutes later – the Island I suppose – He took me for a walk on the beach and showed me the sea. The sea was tame and repetitive and I have to say that sand is pretty boring. There is a lot of it and it all looks very much the same – grain for grain. Dull really. We saw a naked man displaying himself in the dunes. He needn't have bothered for my sake really but it was a nice gesture I suppose.

I can't say that The Island of Purbeck did a lot for me. Seemed much like the rest of my world but some way away which made the day a bit pointless. The best bit was coming back to find Piglet and Kate in the stable yard. Piglet overweight as ever, Kate, practically naked, creosoting the gate in the sunshine. His eyes came out on stalks and He looked a bit overheated. Poor old thing. A good day. I think I'm in His good books – I'll probably make a big mistake again before bed.

12th June

Kate washed her car - we never realised it was a rather nice metallic green as it has always been covered in mud. Once again she was down to practically no clothes for the event which was clearly not good for Him who was saved from a heart attack when Bodgit turned up with his sidekick Scarper who is enormously tall and quite tidy in marked contrast to Bodgit. They had a couple of cups of tea and some of Heather's amazing fruitcake. I think they needed to look at a problem on the roof because they got out a rather unsafe-looking ladder and disappeared. There was some banging and bad language and they came back down again just in time to help Him take the top off the whisky bottle. The three of them rearranged the world noisily and eventually Bodgit and Scarper went home. He tottered off to bed a bit grumpily. I think they are all pretty bad tempered. Kate's OK. Still, you can forgive a dippy blonde more or less everything according to Him. Kate says blondes have more fun. I wonder what she means. Maybe I will go blonde; highlights would do I expect.

I'm pretty sure Blot is in love with me but it's just that she has a funny way of showing it. She spits in a rather coarse way but I realise that we have different cultures and standards. I wiggle a lot and fawn and I can sense that she is impressed - its just that, unlike me, she doesn't like to show her feelings.

15th June

He looked at the stock market prices in the paper this morning. Oh dear! Oh dear! Oh dear! What a gloom set in. I burrowed under the hall chest. He should try living in a world with no rats or rabbits - that would be serious!

I've decided on my tactics so far as the Blot is concerned. At the moment she is very punchy and spits (which as I say is just their way) when I offer to help her with whatever she is doing - which isn't a lot between meals so far as I can see. I'm going to be submissive and fall over on my back - once confidence is established then I can deal with her. I'm pretty sure I remember my mother telling me that no cat walked across her line of sight without permission. And even then she wasn't entirely satisfied that it was in order.

He called me 'officious' and laughed again in that manic way that suggests another of His jokes. I wish He would share them with me but I expect they are as obscure as ever, so perhaps He needn't bother.

18th June

He brushed His hair, what there is of it that is, this morning which should have said something to me I suppose. Anyhow a very old and rather elegant lady came to see us. He was exceedingly deferential in a greasy sort of way; carrying things for her and so on. I've never seen Him behave like that before. I assumed it was his Mother-in-Law - anyhow she brought an absurd girly looking dog with her. It whimped about the place - attached to an amazing expanding sort of line the other end of which was attached to the Lady. I wouldn't tolerate that kind of treatment. God help Him if He tries it on me.

Later, after she had gone, He shook the world by wearing shorts in the garden. With legs like that He could guide incoming aircraft on a dark night. It isn't fair and frightens the more timid of the garden dwellers. My view is that if that is what "They" are like under all those clothes it is a good thing that someone has arranged to cover it all up. Terriers are properly equipped to face the world unencumbered with clothes. However it is probably best not to delve too deeply into Comatose's ill-fitting coat. Who knows what might emerge!

20th June

I helped Him a lot with His gardening today. He was tying things up but some chump had rather inconsiderately, I thought, rolled up the string into a ball so I unrolled it for Him and laid it quite neatly down the lawn. I'm not sure that He appreciated my efforts. The garden is coming on quite nicely. I moved some more stock plants for Him which I thought badly positioned. He got agitated and dashed about the place retrieving the plants in rather an aggressive way. I didn't like His demeanour. I am sure all this emotion could be bad for His blood pressure.

21st June

Today I detected a definite fragileness about Him. He was very quiet and pottered about the place snuffling - He mentioned hay fever but as it rained in the night we can't put it down to pollen. Much more likely a Distillers Company product.

I'm afraid a sticky-out bit needed urgent attention again this morning and in the process of trying to catch it in a series of pirouettes I fell over, grabbed the first thing in sight to steady myself which, unfortunately was part of Bugger Off's anatomy. Bad tempered old cow - there was no need to use that language. Comatose got up briefly, responding to the row and did a pee on His lawn (not normally a good idea). She then subsided back on to my day-bed in front of the Aga. I sometimes wonder just how much life there is in that baggy old body.

24th June

I took one of His land agent's shoes for a walk today. It was very heavy. I'm not surprised He's tired all the time. I abandoned it on the lawn and then it rained. He got cross, mumbled some incomprehensible remarks and tottered off again. I'm not sure why He has them as He does precious little land agency that I have ever detected so a bit of rain in His shoes isn't going to make much difference to Him I would have thought.

I often think that the buttons on His shirts are rather absurd things and need to be removed. He doesn't agree which doesn't surprise me, as He has absolutely no dress sense. He usually comes down in the morning dressed in a riot of discordant colours. I put it down to the fact that His eyes don't function that early in the day and He just chucks on whatever comes to hand first. I have absolutely no doubt that a discerning woman would tidy Him up a bit but it would be an uphill struggle and she'd need to be immune to His more revolting habits.

25th June

I have found a good source of bumblebees. They really are rather quaint and have a comfortable roundness about them; not at all aggressive. They seem to congregate on the catnip. I chased some off and narrowly avoided being bitten back. He yelled again, something to do with giving them a good run for their honey. Another of His obscure jokes I expect rather, spoilt by His accompanying manic laugh which really does give me the willies. He seems out of sorts with me. I'll try to improve but not until tomorrow.

This morning one of the cats (I imagine) left a dead bird in the vegetable garden which I think is quite untidy of it. I brought it to the veranda to show Him. I don't think He was very impressed. As the day wore on and got warmer so the bird acquired a pleasant aroma and became really quite appealing. I redesigned it a bit and left it on the carpet in the hall for Him to admire - He was not in the least impressed, took it outside and tossed it into the shrubbery where He thinks I won't find it. He said it was horrid. How does He know until He has tried it?

28th June

The dog next door who is called Bess came to see me yesterday. I think that it is quite unnecessary to be so big. I don't see the point - no hole could possibly accommodate her. I can't say I took her very seriously. She is even more hairy than either Piglet or me. She has a long droopy tail and a long pointed face. He says that she is a lurcher which I think is a bit personal of Him. Belinda, who owns her, loves her at any rate.

He left a bag of J.Arthur Bower's compost on
the lawn when He was planting up
the pots. The bar code on
it rather irritated me so
I went for it in no
uncertain way. I'm
not quite sure
why now. I
expect there
was a good
reason at the time.
He gave that smile again.
There seem to be so many diversions
it's quite hard sometimes to remember why
one did all sorts of things. I wish He could see that. I ran up the garden and when I got there I looked back. The house seemed rather far away so I ran back. Again He seemed to think that that was amusing. I think He's weird.

29th June

Bugger Off came out on to the lawn this afternoon and sat down. I fixed her with my most gimlet eye from the veranda and charged in a menacing sort of way quite forgetting she wasn't the playful type. She snarled as I careered round her in decreasing circles. Then she slunk off back to the house in a very disdainful way which verged on insulting. She specialises in the art of "skulking". One day when she does that I won't be able to hold back and then she'll be sorry.

I bit His ankle for no obvious reason. I'd rather failed to see that He wasn't wearing socks or trousers for that matter.

Bit of a mistake because I now know what the word 'no' means - not very surprising as He has been using it a lot. Actually I'm beginning to wonder whether He has much of a vocabulary. He's pretty limited in His conversation with me.

1st July

I was chasing after Comatose on our confounded morning walk and my legs got into a tangle and I went head over heels. I expect that it has something to do with the fact that they are getting a bit longer. Anyhow it was really quite a pleasantly disorientating experience - a bit like He feels towards the end of the evening, I rather suspect. He laughed in a worrying sort of way again.

A cat - I imagine it was one of them, unless the Good Lord has taken to dropping manna from heaven - deposited what was left of a squirrel on the veranda. They really are a bit profligate with what is left of their meals, and quite untidy. However I must say it was a terrific toy with a fantastic smell, but very yellow teeth, which rather put me off. I dragged it round the lawn a few times tripping over it's wonderful tail. He, of course, decided that this was not a good toy and threw it into the shrubbery again. Don't they get dull when they get old? I then knocked six bells out of a bantam until he used the 'N' word again.

3rd July

He's forever grubbing about in his vegetable garden. I try to relieve the monotony for Him by pouncing on the rake or hoe or whatever. He doesn't appreciate me. The 'N' word gets thoroughly over-exercised. There was an ugly little plastic sign which said "perpetual spinach" on it. It rather spoiled the rustic atmosphere I thought, so I took it away. Now I can't find it. For some baffling reason He wants it back. I suspect that He forgets where He buries things and has to mark them. His memory seems to be going adding to the list of His fading senses. It is all rather sad really. I bet He doesn't forget where He puts His whisky bottle.

5th July

The garden has a couple of wooden benches at either end of the lawn. I imagine that these are strategically placed to allow Him to totter between them without falling over after a certain time. I helped Kate scrape the paint off one of the benches. She's pretty hopeless at it. It annoyed me that Piglet tried to get in on the act too. He's so dreadfully clumsy. Kate seems pretty free with the 'N' word too. Are they all so inarticulate? By the way, I note that He's got Kate into the garden, working. Until now she's been exclusively in the stable area - where will this all end? There is loose talk about a permanent arrangement come the hunting season. That man 'Blair,' who He grumbles on about, will put a stop to that apparently, and a good thing too - I'm pretty sure His heart wouldn't stand up to it all.

I'm considering a new tactic - a charm offensive. Violence doesn't seem to get to Him. He's fairly thick-skinned except when my canines are brought into action. Ho! Ho!

6th July

He wears these little lace up slipper shoes in the house which frankly look a bit girly. I don't think He has noticed that I'm redesigning them. He'll be pleased in the end. It's just a matter of taste, which I'm sure I will instil into Him in due course.

Belinda is very tall and He says very beautiful. She parks her car outside His side gate. I have developed a new game. I hide under her car and chew away at grass. I know this irritates Him. He always says "you aren't a herbivore damn you" and I look at him with manic eyes. It's a particularly amusing game when He wants to go to bed or when

He's late for an appointment (with a bottle?). It makes Him so mad because He can't get me without getting on His knees in the wet grass and I ignore Him anyway and if a hand gets too close I bite it.

9th July

Someone gave me a small teddy bear – I think it was Belinda who clearly has good taste in toys. I have a great time grabbing it by an ear or something like that and tossing it in the air up the lawn. You can quite imagine that it is alive and I rush up to it and kill it over and over again. By chance I found the teddy under my day bed later on when checking for rabbits. I've decided that it has too many limbs. It'll look quite good soon. Actually it's a toss up whether I redesign His working shoes or the teddy tonight. I have to say the shoes do have a good aroma about them. Talking of work I have yet to see Him do any! I wonder what it is that makes Him mess about for brief periods in his office?

12th July

I had a go at redesigning the runner in the hall this evening. I reckon it's pretty tatty and needs a bit of work on it. He used the 'N' word again so I nipped back for a quick check on rabbits in my day bed. It's getting quite fruity and palatable. I bet Heather puts it in the washing machine – they are all hygiene mad! While working on the runner I was drawn to the stairs which are invitingly straight. I suppose they have to be so that He can get up them easily at the end of the evening. Not a lot of use having corners. I went up them for the first time and a whole new playground opened up. On the left there is a crazy bathroom all red with what He calls "ethnic" pictures all over it. I call them mucky. Off to the right of the stairs is a rabbit warren of bedrooms. I think me and Piglet will have to investigate this part of our world in more detail soon. I suspect that Piglet might have trouble getting his bulky little body up the stairs. One of his problems is that his legs are absurdly short and he is frightfully clumsy.

13th July

He bought me a collar today. A black one. I was not amused. Later He went shopping to Waitrose and I got rid of it. He doesn't know where and I am beginning to forget too. I'm having none of that nonsense. Piglet has a bright blue one. Big wuss. Kate says I should have a pink one. Just try.

He's been with his hunting friends so there'll be a bit of falling over tonight I expect. I think it's time He went to bed - He's beginning to look peculiar.

He has named our sleeping area "the Swamp". It's not at all polite and not always true. I try, but sometimes things get the better of me. Heather does her best to get some sort of human smell back into the room but somehow I nearly always transform it back into a comfortable "doggy" smell.

14th July

I'm not sure what went wrong last night but I rather unusually did two 'you knows' in the Swamp and He was decidedly bad-tempered about it. However, He got over it as soon as this rather smart lady turned up - not his usual sort at all − (no offence to the usual sort) but this one is trendy, dark hair, red lips (and they kissed!) Anyhow, she diverted Him for a time and then, blow me, they put me in the car and we went off together to a derelict house miles away. We had to tramp through jungle high grass, gloomy trees and shrubs all overgrown. They wittered away for absolutely ages ignoring me except for the occasional use of the 'N' word - no rabbits, no fun. He lost his glasses, dotty old man. They probably would have steamed up anyway if He could have found them.

When we got home He found my black collar. NO COMMENT.

16th July

Kate's ill, so He's in a gloom. He has had to do the horses, poor things. It is improbable that He has any idea what He should be doing, but all will be well so long as Kate gets back to work pretty soon; otherwise irreparable damage could be done to the brutes.

I fought a particularly tricky butterfly this morning. He said it was nearly dead when I started on it. What does He know – I was at its level and it was HUGE. It did its best to outwit me but not much does that. It flapped in quite a menacing way with enormous wings, (now and then I had to encourage it's aggression by poking it with my nose). It was dead exciting and what's more He said that it was a RED ADMIRAL. I can have no knowledge of its politics but by all accounts Admirals are truly big. It died. I lost interest. I found a wonderfully mature dead bird soon after and, as instructed by Comatose, I'm perfecting getting the scent to stick to my shoulders by rolling. I know that He will really find my scent irresistible now.

I reckon that after my success with the RED ADMIRAL, I'm ready to take on some big game – moles, stag beetles and the like. The gloves are off!

20th July

He has bought a new toy. A dog brush – its been on His list for weeks but I'm doubtful whether His memory is up to that kind of thing – whisky yes! He never fails to replenish the stocks of whisky. Anyhow, He took to brushing Bugger Off and Comatose. I just don't see the point. It's far too late, they're both nearly dead and their coats, in all honesty, look as if they were a bad buy at a charity shop anyway! If Comatose shakes or moves even slightly suddenly hers could fall off altogether. He made the rather insulting comment that the reason that she eats so much is an attempt to fill the baggy old garment. A sort of joke I suppose.

21st July

It's great to see Him panic when He can't find me. Quite flattering too. Last night I went to bed in Comatose's basket where there is a nice beanbag. Somehow (I recollect rabbits came into it) I got inside the bag and then couldn't find the exit. So I was stuck in there. Well, what a gratifying panic set in. Eventually He was obviously about to have a stroke, so I bellowed, "Here I am" and, thank God for Geors, one of His stepdaughters, whose hearing hasn't passed the point of no return. Because she heard me He rushed in and dug me out. He needed a calming whisky!

23rd July

He keeps 'ridging up' the potatoes in His vegetable garden - I think they look ludicrously military so I un-ridged them so to speak. He doesn't like that. He's not too keen on the military so I thought I'd be doing Him a favour. I think He's pretty ungrateful. It is very hard to know what to do for the best. The trouble is things have a habit of just happening so then I have to either run for cover or face it. That's where the teeth come in handy.

Geors seems to be back from school for the holidays. She and Kate are cast to some extent in the same mould - as He puts it, "both blonde and dippy." I have to say she is out an awful lot of the time and reappears in the mornings looking pretty terrible, like Him. However I think she has a goodish time so perhaps Kate is right and I will go blonde.

Bodgit cycled down on his rickety old bicycle this evening to discuss something to do with the Estate and as usual it had to be done at the kitchen table over a bottle. They got round a fair few glasses and then Bodgit wobbled his way home. He made a notional and barely audible comment about stopping drinking and pottered off to bed.

24th July

He went off all day yesterday to the Game Fair. I'd have thought He was a good deal too old for games so I took the opportunity to chew a bit off His Garry Rhodes cookery book. Looks much more lived in now. He'll be quite pleased when He gets back I expect.

I hear that no-hoper called 'Blair' is seriously trying to stop hunting. Where on earth are his basic instincts? Hasn't he felt the buzz of a receding mole as he tears at it's hole with his teeth (and by all accounts he has more than his fair share of them!) or the sheer joy of teasing a beetle (makes me chuckle the way they just carry on trying to scuttle for cover, even though you have removed half their legs) I stalk the blackbirds on the lawn, dodging between table and chair legs and the statuary – what a gas. And Blair wants to stop it! What a grey, dull world he's trying to create. They say he goes to Tuscany for his holidays – Poor Tuscans they really don't deserve him, so He says. Blair should come rabbiting with me, that would put some fizz in his blood (if he's got any).

25th July

His "I'm never going to have another drop of whisky" didn't last long. A couple of His hunting friends turned up last night. Pledges don't last long in those circumstances. They had to be shown the garden by Him. They walked up the long border, glasses firmly gripped in their hands, then disappeared into the vegetable garden and reappeared some minutes later in unsteady fashion looking, in rather a glazed way, at the rose pergola on the other side. It's amazing how many whiskies seemed necessary for that little bout of exercise.

I had just got His log pile to a nice shape and of easy ascent when He rearranged it and put a whole lot more wood on it. He's got a bee in his bonnet about tidiness in the garden. Anyhow, the upshot is I've got to make it more appealing and lower by spreading the wood around. I'll start tomorrow. There must be something chaseable in there, as the aroma is quite distinctive but of what I have yet to discover.

He went into raptures about me doing a 'you know' in the field. It really is odd what pleases Him. Anyhow, long may it deflect from the 'Toblerone' wrapper I'm trying to hide in the sitting room, having eaten its contents. He is mad about Toblerone and has withdrawal symptoms if He doesn't get it after supper, rather as He does if He sees the level in the bottle getting dangerously near the bottom. The wrapper has been under every chair but none of them seems to provide total concealment. If only He didn't buy the jumbo size it would all be much less troublesome. I'll have to apply the charm tactic but it is wearing a bit thin.

28th July

A huge dog came down the lane yesterday attached to his master's bicycle by a bit of bailer twine so that his lazy master didn't have to pedal. At just about the worst moment the dog saw a cat. Master, dog, bicycle and cat went into low orbit for a time. There was a terrible lot of noise and yelling by the cat's owner who is an odd foreign man. They're all a bit odd in this village He says, which is pot calling the kettle black, in my view. Anyhow He thought it would be the end, in a rather bloody way, of an ancient and much loved moggy. So He dragged me off to the village shop before the final denouement. I was pretty cross because I really wanted to see the fur fly. We still don't know if the stupid animal survived or if it got torn limb from limb and whether there are now some pleasantly decaying bits knocking about the place.

1st August

Geors has some seriously ugly shoes. I've done her a real favour by redesigning them but He thinks she's not going to be pleased. In fact not to put too fine a point on it He reckons she'll go ballistic whatever that means. Aren't people ungrateful?

He says He can't understand why I have to chew everything – I wonder if has He ever tried?

He's done it again. He's planted up that terracotta pot with – can you believe – wallflowers. He thought He had been cunning and hidden it in the vegetable garden. How silly. Anyhow, that's dealt with and there can be no argument. I did this entirely on my own without Piglet's help. Incidentally, Kate turned up yesterday to all intents and purposes naked. I have to say, I don't think her legs were any less beacon-like than His, but oh dear, you should have seen Him. Steam came out of His ears again. It won't do Him any good.

You know it's really not fair. I've been presented with a garden full of moving targets like the bantams and (when they aren't looking) the cat, but because of the 'N' word, I'm reduced to playing with plastic toys that make silly little squeaky noises and fluffy teddy bears (which have lost all appeal to me) – how ignominious – no street cred there.

2nd August

I've got Him on the run so far as food is concerned – there was an egg in my lunch today. It's very hot and sunny and after a lunch like that I rather developed springs in my legs in the long grass – there could be dozens of rabbits out there. Anyhow, He chased me in a rather juvenile way – not funny – and made a silly remark about "Mad dogs and Englishmen." I can't say I saw the joke. I could have understood it perfectly if the adjective had been attached to the other noun!

5th August

I caught my first rodent today. An enormous rat. Time for a serious celebration I should have thought. I have to say it wasn't very difficult – it didn't move very fast– actually it didn't move at all because it was dead but I haven't told Him that – He went into raptures. I suspect one of the cats caught it and it died of fright when it heard I lived here too. It obviously then proved too much for the cats so I'm dealing with it now. They need me, I can see that.

He has penned up some of the bantams. I imagined that it was for my amusement so that I could taunt them through the wire of their cage more easily and save a lot of rushing round the garden. However when I menace them through the wire mesh He got very agitated and brought out the hunting whip. Honestly, you never know where you are with Him. I am reduced to redesigning a plastic flowerpot - what ignominy. Talking of flowerpots, his beloved Kate ran a wheelbarrow into one of his posh terracotta pots and broke it into little bits, the pot that is. He just laughed in that manic way of His. If I'd done that while about my business of keeping the garden free of riff raff, He'd certainly have got the whip out. There really is a good case for going blonde I think.

6th August

He nearly blew a gasket today. He was working at a farm near Windsor where there are polo ponies and it was truly hot. We went off to look at trees as usual, which in itself seems a fairly repetitive, boring job, and when we came back to the car there was a tall leggy girl hosing down a steaming pony. She was wearing the shortest hot pants He had seen since the seventies, and not a lot else. I got quite worried about Him for a time and rather wished she would turn the hose onto Him. He said that He isn't going to that part of the world again because He's scared of all the fearsome women in huge four wheel drive cars driving earnestly about the place in a hurry to pick up their 2.4 children from private schools. More like He couldn't take too many polo pony grooms in hot weather!

7th August

Comatose is really coming round to me now. She doesn't seem to mind me nipping her skirts. Old Bugger Off is thoroughly ill tempered still - even He thinks she's a bad tempered old bitch and tells her so. Her language is dreadful and coarse. No breeding. I think her bed is pretty dull – just a bit of carpet in a square so I'm bringing my designer skills into play and rearranging it. He has not said anything yet. I expect He's saving his words of praise until I've finished the job. Heather keeps picking up all the chewed off bits, which is jolly decent of her. I expect she appreciates my aesthetic abilities. In this hot weather she too has taken to coming to work in shorts and not much else. By the way He looks at both of them I think the weather ought to turn cold and wet quite soon.

8th August

We went on safari today. First over the home field where the grass is now very long and wet – not much fun because it is very hard walking but then we went into a sort of Savannah region with close cropped grass (grazed no doubt by large fierce animals of the night) surrounded by huge trees. Apparently this is the park next to the big house where Bodgit lives with his long-suffering wife. At the far end where the Savannah gives way to near jungle conditions, I got the fright of my life as I more or less stepped on a seriously large bird. He said it was "just a partridge" – more like an eagle if you ask me. Anyhow, after that I was more careful and watchful and I "used my nose." It's a saying of His so I use it here in case it is significant.

The jungle consists of huge oak trees and hazel coppice. We went into it along a path that was barely a path at all – all overgrown and really quite tricky. There is no doubt about it, my legs will have to grow a bit if I am to get the best out of this place. Comatose was quite animated for her. She is supposed to be a gun dog after all and this is the place He brings His gun and her, apparently. Bugger Off is clearly out of her natural element, whatever that might be, and should not be let loose in such a hostile and potentially interesting environment. I, however, found the whole experience quite excellent. It was very dark and there were mysterious noises and new smells. Huge birds flapped noisily out of their roosts in the trees. At one point there was a large watering hole – Comatose, who is not very subtle, plunged in and having had her fill then did a 'you know' in it – jolly antisocial. I gave it a miss.

We came to a sort of jungle lodge. Then something happened that I never thought I would see. Comatose suddenly brightened up and actually jumped over a fence! After I had recovered from that shock I went through it and suddenly the most enormous bird with a long trailing tail got up angrily and shot over our heads with a fearful cry. Must have been nothing less than a vulture disturbed on its victim's corpse! Phew! What an excitement.

After that my blood was up and as soon as we got back to the garden I had a go at a couple of mole hills, tore across the garden, scattering a few bantams and put some rabbits into a hole in my outside-bed.

I hope we do that again! Soon!

11th August

This has been the worst day of my life. He's been really cruel. He went out all the morning leaving me shut in, then He let me out and went off with some friends and I do know I shouldn't have succumbed to the temptation but they are so inviting so I chased the bantams and one went all floppy. When He came back, I brought him the corpse. I'd rather forgotten that I shouldn't have and I was really quite proud. BUT OH DEAR! He beat me with a stick. I made a frightful noise and hid. After a bit He seemed to have calmed down so I helped Him in the garden AND THEN I just couldn't resist it. I chased them again. He nearly broke a blood vessel and this time He hit me twice with the stick – that did hurt and He threatened to give me to a family who live in a high rise flat in Birmingham. I wish I were dead. Life really isn't worth living – I don't even find solace in digging for moles. It's all so unfair and depressing.

14th August

I caught an enormous snake today. He said it was a 'slow worm'. It certainly wasn't a worm and it was only slow because it was dead. Where does He get his information from? I sometimes wonder whether He ever had an education. Anyhow, as usual He took it away and tossed it into the bushes.

We went on another trip to the jungle and the smells are becoming even more interesting. There was a very dark part with a track through it. He said it was a deer track - I couldn't see why He needed to be so affectionate about it. Anyhow, I found a wonderful dead bird and Comatose gave me further lessons on how to roll in it shoulder blade down. He got very excited and it made Him mad. He kept mentioning "Eau de oiseau mort", whatever that means but He was pleased with what was presumably some sort of joke. He still takes a quite unnecessary interest in my bowel movements. I wish He'd mind His own business. It's really very personal and unnecessary.

15th August

He spends quite a lot of time laughing at me which I still find unnerving. I was dealing with a clothes peg under the chest in the hall which seemed to a amuse Him. Very odd. Another thing: I had dug this really neat hole in the lawn and He comes out all steamy and says "What's this then?" and I say "It's a hole - I don't regard that as a very testing concept so long as you've got eyes." And He's quite grumpy. It was an extremely good hole. Notice the past tense here – He went and filled it in. I don't know what to do with Him sometimes. Later on I found a nest of ants on the veranda - they really are whizzy little things. I ate a good few - not really terribly tasty but different. The ones that got in amongst my fur got me really mad - it was like having your trousers on fire.

17th August

The last twenty-four hours have been a bit of a disaster! Yesterday He shot another pigeon in the garden but it fluttered off into the shrubbery in a rather feeble way, so He got out Comatose His trusty gun dog and sent her in. She made a few half-hearted attempts to find the hapless bird. Then I went in, and even I could tell that in there, somewhere, was the pigeon. Comatose gave up and pottered off

towards the house looking bored and tired in the hope that she'd make
the sanctuary of her bed before collapsing. She eventually fell asleep
on the lawn. Anyway to cut a long story short I found the corpse and
very delicious it was too. What remained I put under the Laburnum
tree on the lawn and, replete, fell to sleep on a bed of feathers and
aromatic body parts, all pleasantly bloody.
He woke me up at one point and laughed
- I'm beginning to be troubled by that
laugh. Well the inevitable happened. I did
both 'you knows' overnight and He was
very decent about it. I think He was
hit by an unusual attack of
conscience. He muttered
something about "Should
have found the corpse and
disposed of it myself I
expect".

18th August

He took me to the airfield. He is not supposed to let me loose on the
field but now and then when no one is looking I get to nose round
the hangars and chat up anyone who will talk to me. This was not one
of those occasions. He disappeared for a couple of hours - that was
OK I suppose but then He went to see a new stockbroker and the sun
got to me at about the same time that both my lunch and yesterday's
pigeon got to my inside bits and Oh dear! In his lovely Mercedes. I
can't believe He was so good. Conscience again? Later Kate turned
up (better dressed) and was very smug about Piglet. Never does that
kind of thing - I bet he does and if not I can only assume he doesn't
get my varied diet! He needs to get a life (Piglet that is).

I have to admit to a bit of insomnia. It's quite simple - Comatose
snores - dear oh dear, how she snores. Her bed vibrates with the
dreadful noise. I'm really quite bleary eyed in the mornings. A bit like
Kate after one of her weekend parties or Him more or less every
morning. He's quite nice to Kate then and gives her cups of tea and
lets her have slices of the wonderful fruitcake Heather bakes for Him.

He keeps the cake in what He imagines is a secret place but which everyone knows! He doesn't seem to notice the gradual reduction. He's practically dead so I suppose He wouldn't notice. I'm not mad about my dorm, "the Swamp." Piglet told me in very great confidence that he sleeps on Kate's bed. I'm not telling Him - He'd blow a fuse.

21st August

We have had a swarm of bees in the vegetable garden today, quite close to where I eat the odd putrid corpse. I expect they had heard that I'd taken up residence here and thought that I was worth a visit. He took a widely circuitous route round them - what a wimp. I have to say that I gave them plenty of opportunity to admire me by standing under their swarming place and they ignored me to a man. I really can't think why they came - they need not bother again. They make a silly noise anyway. He says they sting - let them try!

I managed to sneak into the village shop today when He went in for His boring old Telegraph. It is a marvellous tin shack crammed with delicious smelling things just down the road from our house. I expect He chose His house in this position so that He could get His paper and other essentials like whisky without having to totter too far. They stupidly display some delicious sweets near the floor and being conveniently small (but beautifully marked of course!) I got quite a mouthful and hid under a display cabinet and ate them. It was dead nice. I don't think anyone noticed.

22nd August

I'll tell you what I am finding really very good sport (and what is life if not for sport - I hope our wimpy government will take that message on board) and that's Molehilling. You just have to nudge the top layer of soil with your nose and nine times out of ten the most delicious aroma of rodent hits the nostrils. I can dig out a hill to such an extent that I can get quite a lot of me into it in no time at all. I practise my digging on His lawn - not popular with Him but good practise. Now and then I find a carelessly abandoned dead mole - good to cart about to increase one's street cred if you meet a cat or whatever. He always gets them off me and tosses them into the shrubbery. What a feast awaits me there one day!

He described me as "having been quite a challenge." I didn't care for the tone of His voice and, come to think of it, what's all this past tense?

23rd August

Piglet tells me that he's developed a new game. He buries things in the back of Kate's car to see how mad she gets. His best thing ever was her lighter, so she couldn't smoke which nearly drove her potty. It sounds a good sport and I'm lining up things I can hide of His. If I hid His whisky I'd cause a rare panic – like a crash on the stock market only worse. I've discovered a ruse that really irritates Him. After our last thing at night walk I scuttle under the little chest in the hall to

avoid being put to bed in the Swamp. He thinks He can flush me out by pretending to take us all for another walk. He must think I was born yesterday. O.K. it wasn't that long ago, but I'm not as stupid as He might think. Sadly He is just able to pick up the chest and even though I move about under it with it so to speak, He does manage to scoop me up. I have to admit that for some reason it is becoming more and more of a squeeze to get under the chest. I suppose I'm beginning to develop in all sorts of ways and it may be only a matter of time before I can no longer take refuge there.

25th August

He was quite rightly a bit grumpy with Belinda's bantam cockerel today. It appeared on the trellis in His garden from where it flew down to near the two bantam hens, ran at them, raped them and then just to compound the felony flew at poor disabled Wonky Donkey, the resident bantam cock making him wobble down the lawn in a disjointed sort of way. I thought it was all quite distasteful and He went out brandishing the hunting whip. Just for once I think that I am on His side so far as that whip is concerned but He need not get complacent about it.

31st August

He went away this weekend to Suffolk. He didn't ask my permission and, what's more, he left Geors in charge. She didn't have a clue. Meals of indeterminate nature served at all sorts of times. But I didn't starve.

He tipped up on Monday afternoon and greeted me as if I was supposed to have missed Him and pleased to see Him. Who does He think He is? What kind of fellow goes off for the weekend leaving a couple of dippy blondes in charge? I was disdainful. I strutted passed Him and looked bored. The trouble is I was actually very pleased to see Him. I had to keep my feelings fairly low key. He went off for a drink at the big house with Bodgit and his wife and I went for a sleep in the spare bedroom. He went nearly mad looking for me when He came home – lots of whisky fumes preceded Him. I lay on my back on the bed and nearly wet myself giggling. Kate turned up clapped out from dancing at a rugby Ball in Bristol. Two days later her eyes still looked glazed. He, of course, didn't seem to notice which only goes to prove just about everything.

4th September

The helicopter bug has struck again and the sun is shining, so we get to see Him less and less. He went out with a woman tonight. I wonder if she's suitable. I'm just a little apprehensive – I hope she knows what she's letting herself in for. I think we'll have to keep a watching brief. He got back very late and expected me to get out of bed and go for a walk. Flushed with some sort of supposed success He thinks He can get us all out of bed just to hear about his evening - very immature if you ask me!

Geors failed her driving test today. I sort of wanted to console her so I lay on the sofa while she bleated for hours to one of her friends on her mobile phone which, by the way, looks for all the world as if it has been spot-welded to the side of her head.   He will go mad when the bill comes in. I wish she would learn because He gets quite cross about phone bills. I bet His drink bills don't bear too close scrutiny.

I can still get under the chest in the hall, JUST.

7th September

It was hot and sunny again today so Kate was only partially dressed. I don't think it's really fair of her because I do depend on Him, for the time being at least, and if she goes on like this He will have a heart attack and pop off. Then who'd feed me?

I really irritated Geors last night while He was out with His new woman (who is still a secret) by going under and behind the dresser in the kitchen which they conveniently boxed when they moved into this house centuries ago leaving a tunnel behind. I often nip in there when He is bad tempered. They call it the rat run; not an oblique reference to me I hope. She was worried that I had done a runner and that He would be upset and cross. I find that concept gratifying but I won't let on.

8th September

I had a terrific battle with Piglet during the course of which he knocked out one of my canine teeth. So Pig' says that's OK because you'll get the tooth fairy tonight - so I quizzed him on this subject about which I am ignorant and, blow me, he's practically a millionaire in dog biscuits from losing his first teeth while I wallow in penury. I'm afraid I take a very dim view.

Friday 10th September

No signs of that tooth fairy. Stupid Piglet. Stupid fairy.

He's been flying his silly little helicopter today which always puts Him in a good mood. He landed in the field at the end of the garden again so I went out to see Him. I got out through the kitchen window which is an escape route that Piglet and I have developed. Piglet has found out how to unlatch it. They look bewildered when we turn up after they have apparently locked us in. I thought He was less than welcoming when He bundled us back into the house through the kitchen window and locked it properly, and then He took Kate off for a ride. I can't see the point of it all - no mole holes, no moles, just a lot of noise. I have a niggling feeling He's trying to impress someone. Fat chance!

I'm quite depressed. It suddenly struck me that I'd learnt not to chase, let alone kill, the bantams and I feel that its a bit of a betrayal of my status as a "fearless killer." If I ever wanted to join the T.A. (Terriers Anonymous) I'm not sure that my record regarding practically static live targets would stand up. I mean it really is quite frustrating and ignominious.

Thursday 16th September

This is written in retrospect - yesterday was a bad day. It all started with them cutting the grass in Home field, then He popped down in his silly little helicopter so I had to go out there and see it (still shiny and noisy). Anyhow, having cut the grass, this has exposed a positive treasure trove of dead and deliciously putrid birds, mice, beetles and so on. All out there for the ingesting - so I did. I spent ages hoovering up the field. I then had rather a rich lunch. It all came back again all over the place so to speak and I had such a sore tummy all day.

He fed me less richly in the evening and I have to say I'm better now but it does seem rather as if I lurch from one disaster to the next. In my philosophical moments I wonder whether this is the pattern of my life to be. The 'N' word is still heard pretty often.

He keeps asking me "Why are you permanently in trouble?" and I answer that I'm not, it's He who thinks I am. It's a matter of perception. Why can't He see that?

17th September

Do you know sometimes I can sit on the veranda and positively police what's going on in the garden. Great sense of power. There's an insufferable blackbird or two who wantonly strut across the lawn in my full view. It's just not on and I will have to deal with them but probably not until tomorrow.

He went quite ecstatic about the fact that I cleaned up my supper tonight. He's really very odd the way mundane things seem to please Him. Anyhow, for the first time ever, I was given food, properly cut up into bite-sized morsels with chicken stock gravy. It was a whole lot better than the usual dry irregularly lumped bits with dry biscuits looking remarkably like rabbit droppings and tasting like cardboard – even His shoes are tastier. Well, full marks to Him. I hope He keeps this standard up.

20th September

He has, and I'm eating much more and I know that the Lovely Kate thinks I'm hyperactive anyhow, but I have to say the energy levels are suddenly even higher.

The weekends seem to be not much more than a procession of unattached women of indeterminate age, with or without offspring. Last weekend there were two and a youth. This Saturday it was one, plus a couple of teenage daughters and, horror of horrors, a couple of enormous dogs. At first I was horrified and quite cross and there was a lot of grumbling from the usually recumbent Comatose and the perpetually crabby Bugger Off. She remains very evil-tempered. Comatose went back to asleep again quite soon and Bugger Off slunk off into the house, so it was left to me to sort out this rabble. They made the mistake (as did I, but I've matured of course) of thinking that the bantams are purely there as live target practice. These 'lurchers' settled down eventually but not before the birds got plenty of flying hours in their log books!! Ho! Ho! There was an enforced march to the jungle but the lurchers ran riot through the thickest parts and I had to keep my eyes and ears open to see that the game was not too disturbed. There was a lot of giggling from her and a fair bit of 'Darling'-ing from Him. All very unnecessary in my opinion. I'm glad to say sanity was restored when the teenage daughters started to grumble, and she decided to take them and the two absurd lurchers home - I didn't realise how much I valued the peace and quiet of my garden.

24th September

He's talking about buying a house in France. I gave him fair warning that I'm NOT joining any European community of dogs. I can NOT yap in French and I'm not learning - they can jolly well discourse in English. I bet French moles taste garlicky. Quite revolting. I think this is a BAD idea - His idea of a joke was to tell me that I might have to be electronically chipped. Sounds very uncomfortable.

After a quiet day yesterday and a good night's sleep, I got up pretty bouncy this morning. I found a wonderfully old mole in the field which He took off me for no better reason than I had got it in my mouth I suspect and proceeded to refer to me as "Miss Whizzy Knickers". I'm not at all sure that He should refer to my undergarments in that way or in any way come to think of it.

By any standards, we had a pretty busy weekend and do you know, Comatose remained asleep or more or less asleep the entire time. She gets up, goes for her mandatory walk in the field, after which she conks out again in her bed, only getting up from time to time to allow the blood to get back into her nooks and crannies. She does however get up with huge enthusiasm for her supper, after which it's back to a state of mental and physical near-death. I can't see the point of going on. He says that's the way Labradors are, in which case I can't see the point of Labradors.

26th September

I've perfected the art of turning the laundry basket over and pinching socks. It's a doddle and I'll have to tell Piglet. Talking of whom, Kate is getting browner and browner – she's almost foreign. He just continues to look overheated.

Last night I completely lost control and whizzed round the sitting room like a dingbat. He looked on in amazement. I have to say I wasn't too sure what got into me either. Comatose opened a weary eye and Bugger Off retreated to a darker corner. It was all very exciting and I did an unusual 'you know' over night in the swamp. It was only today when Piglet reminded me that we had found a cache of bantams' eggs that I realised what had fired the engine last night! The old chap has been a bit 'sotto voce' after a sleepless night thinking He'd lost an air ticket to Newcastle and worrying about who would look after us. Kate's done the dirty by going off to Cardiff with a bunch of Rugby players. I suppose it will be matchsticks keeping their eyes open tomorrow for both of them but for different reasons. Ho! Ho! Ho! I'm thinking of going even more blonde – seems to give one a head start by a mile.

28th September

I developed a new tactic in the car today. I launched myself from the back seat onto His right shoulder and when, as is inevitable, He darted forward wondering "What on earth was that?, I snuggled down between Him and the seat and watched nicely out of His side window at the world unfolding. It threw Him into complete confusion and a lot of bad words came out. After that I decided to roll on my back on the seat next to Him and looked appealing – one snag – the gear lever knob is just at tooth height so I wrapped my two now resplendent sets of teeth round it and rolled my eyes. When He saw that He nearly had a heart attack! It seems that a minor nudge of the thing northwards so to speak would throw the whole car into reverse with fascinating results.
When me and Piglet come in from the garden He grumbles that we have dirty socks on and gets pretty fed up when in the course of a perfectly innocent game of tag in His bedroom we leave foot prints all

over His sheets. Actually Heather got pretty mad at us once because He shut us out of His room so we were forced to use the bedroom Heather uses as a laundry room. It's good in there as you can get right round without touching the floor so long as you use the blanket box by the window too. Unfortunately that is where Heather puts the basket containing the sheets after washing, and it has been known for us to leave our marks on them too which causes a 'housekeeping problem' it seems. The severity of the fuss is disproportionate to the crime in my opinion.

4th October

He was away this weekend – burying His mother, he said. Well, me and Piglet had a rare old time. The modest hole in the lawn has nearly reached the status of a quarry. Both of us can get a head down at the same time.

Geors was in charge of us with a bit of help from June who is unofficial village Mayor. She has a strawberry farm at the far end of the lane and very little happens here without her knowledge and tacit approval. She is one of the few people in the village who really does seem to have a busy working life. The meals were a bit hit and miss and though it irks me to say so, I did miss Him a bit and I just HOPE I didn't overdo the welcome home bit. You can bet your boots there was a woman at the burying ceremony. He looked tired but too well for it to have been just a funeral.

He says his sons (are there really more like him?) are coming to stay with their dogs. Now, this may not be a good idea. I hope they aren't too big – any of them.

He's absolutely got supper right tonight. How did He know I like courgettes and runner beans cooked in butter? Good of Him to have gone to so much trouble for me. Incidentally I find His continuing fascination with my more fundamental activities quite intrusive and His delight at my success quite unwarranted. Jolly personal, I call it.

5th October

I've decided that the ENORMOUS dog Bess next door is really a great pal. I've found my way through a maze of fencing which I suspect was deliberately put there to make escape if not impossible, quite an adventure. The problem is He hasn't realised that to a Jack Russell, barriers are to be overcome either by going through, under or if really necessary, over. It has to be said that under is more of an adventure. You never know who or what you might meet. Anyhow having got through, the idea is that Bess digs up, out of her garden, a fantastically tasty bone of unimaginable size and we share it. Some are better than others but it doesn't much matter what their size is, it's their taste and state of putrification which matter. He can't understand and I do explain it to Him. For some reason He's not keen on me kissing Him at the moment.

Geors is back from The Bahamas and she's rather a disgusting brown colour. She has also obviously had a fright as her hair has gone sort of white. I think people, particularly men of a certain age, feel sorry for her because they look at her rather a lot.

8th October

He says that today is His birthday. I couldn't understand why there was such a big post and a long time was spent cooking. Then, surprise! surprise! a completely new woman turns up to celebrate. I really can't understand where they all come from. Maybe you can get them at Waitrose in a little package and then all He has to do is re-hydrate them. I suppose that way He gets to choose the sort He likes. I wonder if they get any say in the matter. This shopping seems rather fun. Anyhow I shouldn't have thought such antiquity was anything to celebrate. I think I'd keep pretty quiet if I was Him.

Getting through the fence to see Bess usually ends up with my fur coat being rather laden with little sticky burrs that seem to grow in the rough bits of His garden. They itch and I have to spend ages scratching. He makes gratuitous comments about some of my lodgers being on the move. I think that's quite offensive and in any case He's

not the tidiest thing on two legs Himself. In fact not to put too fine
a point on it He is only marginally tidier than Bodgit and he is
legendarily scruffy.

12th October

He, Geors and Kate went off to a hunter trials. He was a fence judge
and took all us dogs with him. He attached Piglet and me to the tow
bar on the back of the Subaru - Comatose passed out on a seat and
Bugger Off skulked. It was amazingly boring - no blood, no crashes,
no moles that I saw and not a pheasant on the horizon. I have to say
that if they really do enjoy sitting all day watching horses going round
the same course time and again it just reinforces my view that most of
them are indeed brain-dead.

Anyhow, Kate and Geors messed about
with horses. Kate was due to ride Spider
(the absurdly enormous blackish horse)
round the course, which eventually she
did. He got dangerously over-excited
when she appeared. He fired off some
photographs and then subsided again
behind the Sunday newspapers, only
coming rather slowly to life again when
the next competitor appeared. Now and
then some over-friendly female turned
up, one with smoked salmon sandwiches
for Him - He became really animated at
that point and there was some quite
unnecessarily loud kissing and laughing - He's so obvious- at which
point He really turns on the charm. It's enough to make you puke -
talking of which, Piglet did, in His lorry, and I got to clear it up -
yummy! Anyhow, He nearly had a stroke when it transpired that Kate
won - she got a silver cup and some loot and a rude red rosette. He
could hardly contain himself. He fell short of giving her a public snog
but it caused Him to go a funny colour for a time. I suppose it had
nothing to do with Spider who had to nip and tuck over, round and
through twenty or more obstacles.

Friday 15th October

He's been quite difficult this week. He says it's lack of sleep. He has had a medical and wishing to present his best body, he gave up whisky - ask no more. Also He was out three nights on the trot - once with the new woman - they must be desperate. My bet is that He has to have new ones because they only go out with Him once which is more than enough for the poor creatures. I could save them the trouble if only they'd ask.

17th October

The garden was becoming seriously interesting with hazards and toys everywhere. He decided to put in some time tidying it up this weekend (no more desperate women) and now the 'N' word gets used a whole lot more. I wish He could be more consistent.

He's suddenly started taking a bit more notice of His appearance, although in my book it's too little too late. Anyhow it could be that one of these women is getting to Him (or at Him more like!!). I caught Him looking at Himself in the hall mirror, WITH HIS GLASSES ON. Not a pretty sight and a tiny bit worrying. Some of His hunting friends are coming round tonight. Presumably one of them is the reason for all this sprucing up!

Aren't they noisy? One of the women with a cackle not normally heard outside a turkey farm and the men got steadily louder and louder. Then they took up bumping into things. Afterwards He took us for a peremptory walk and then He eventually fell into bed. And oh dear! what a mess He will look tomorrow morning; talk about the red planets, He seems to have one on either side of His incandescent nose. I bet I get a lot of "I'm cutting out the whisky" again. Lasts until six o'clock that does. No self discipline - it'll be His downfall (Ha! Ha!).

19th October

Today He has tried to occupy me or shut me in to prevent me visiting Bess next door. I'm not quite sure why, but I bet it has something to do with not being able to raise His voice to call me back for whatever reason because of the delicate state of His head. He's not very subtle so as soon as He did let me out I was round there more or less as fast as my legs would take me.

He took us for a walk in the jungle and it really does become more and more interesting. Comatose shambles along huffing and puffing while Bugger Off just looks out of place. The squirrels are just like rabbits that run up trees - rather unsporting really and I'm not sure I'm into heights. He'd better not take me flying.

He's got 'Emma' coming to supper. He's spent two days preparing the meal. I hope its better than some of the ones He does for me. You'd think she was Royalty. He's chucked Geors out and told her not to come back for twenty-four hours (gosh, what optimism) and He's tidied up the house.

20th October

Well, I think His choice is quite good - she played with me most of the time. The food smelt good but boy oh boy He's tired today! In fact rather than battle with me over Bess, He bundled us all into the car and took us to work with Him which turns out to be not much more than walking round some woods. Not very taxing. I hope no one has to pay Him too much. We then had a very nice walk in the New Forest, which wasn't wet and cold and as ghastly as last time. I don't know why they call it a Forest - not many trees. He's absolutely worn out this evening.

This morning I had my 'whizzy knickers' on again. I lead Him a great dance round the village all over the Mayor's strawberry fields and into Belinda's garden and so on. I could tell He was desperate to get back so I was especially uncatchable! I love to see the manic look come into His eyes. It is at about this time, straight after breakfasting on vitamin pills, that He goes into a little room and reads. Sort of ritual I expect - probably has religious connotations.

21st October

He went out in his helicopter again today and came to the village to pick up a couple of teenage girls. I'm beginning to worry about Him. He looked quite pleased with Himself when He finally touched ground after His flying - its rather pathetic really.
I'm in trouble again. There's a really delicious big (well it was big) carpet under the dining room table. A bit scruffy round the edges and in my attempt to tidy it up, bits came away in my teeth, so to speak. Well, there's no hiding what isn't there and He noticed the shortening and really went over the top. It seems that it was a carpet given to his Mother by an Ethiopian King more than fifty years ago. In my view that means it well past its sell by date and should be replaced anyway. It seems that there is a perfectly good carpet shop at Wilton which is no distance away where He could get a nice new one. Anyhow He says that if it should ever get discovered it will be Fish in chains in a dungeon in Addis Ababa and eventually finding my way on to an Ethiopian dinner plate with an orange in my mouth (at best).

He says I whiff a bit of the countryside but not of honeysuckle. I'm not sure that's much of a compliment. I'll give it some thought but not till tomorrow at the earliest; I have an appointment with one of Bess's bones and it is a particularly good vintage.

23rd October

I have to admit that His meals have improved but I am not at all sure that He should refer to me as "squat". He also said that I was a complete mess and that He thought I needed to be valeted. I don't know what it means but it doesn't sound very comfortable. I'll give that some thought too.

He went out in a big helicopter today with his son and daughter-in-law, who are visiting. He came back looking exhausted. I think He's too old for all that kind of thing. He's not really the jet set type (too scruffy). They went to the Isle of Wight for tea. He claimed He'd taken them abroad - He's got a weird sense of adventure. I'm still not convinced that the Island of Purbeck is abroad.

26th October

His mother-in-law (first time round) is ill, so He went off to Worcestershire to see her. I wonder if she wants to see Him - however, that's another story (I expect). He took us all with him. Comatose and B-O dozed their way to and from the place, but I had a wonderful time keeping an eye on the driving of other cars, both in front and behind.

There is the most wonderful place for me between the front seats in his car which I'm sure was designed for me. He says it's supposed to be an armrest. But He uses his other arm for His whisky glass, so why does He need a 'rest' for his un-exercised arm? He calls the armrest the 'Fish Perch' and goes off into gales of laughter at some obscure private joke I suppose. Don't get it myself. I have to say most of His driving wasn't too bad, but now and then some of it was diabolical and it became very erratic so I assumed He'd seen a pretty blonde until I looked at Him and saw that He was barely awake (dreaming of blondes maybe). He was out last night and I bet He hit the whisky and that had made Him sleepy. He was a bit like Comatose! In fact He is often a bit like Comatose in a lot of respects. Most of His clothes are as ill-fitting and elderly. It was rather pathetic really because He had to stop in a motorway service station car park and go to sleep while we all bit our claws wondering if He would remember supper time. When we got to Worcestershire I gave his ex-wife's dog, called Susie (rather a whimpy thing of indeterminate breeding) a good deal of stick. She pats you with her feet either in greeting or maybe aggression it's hard to tell. I expect her teeth are made of rubber. It was all rather gloomy and I assume that the prognosis for the mother-in-law is bad. I'll be glad to get back to porcine Piglet and I bet He will be pleased to get the chance to chat up Kate again.

27th October

He is in the impolite habit of referring to some of the livestock that find their way into my fur as "lodgers." Anyhow on our morning walk today I rather got carried away and was whizzing down the Home Field when one or more of my alleged lodgers got on the move too and set up a frightful itching. Well it's quite difficult to deal with them in these circumstances and it was silly of me to try. I did a half turn to have a go at a particularly irritating one, went head over heels cannoned into Bugger Off who snapped at me, Comatose looked at me wearily and He was reduced to wild, intemperate laughter. I didn't recover my dignity for quite a long time.

1st November

He had a party in the garden at the weekend and I don't think He's quite recovered. Very dozy. He's quite liveable with for a change. One has to wonder if romance is in the air. He danced with endless very young girls and on Sunday He had a bad back - serve Him right, dirty old man. He kept showing everyone His fairy lights - up in the garden trees (the lights that is - not Him, though He was high as a kite most of the time!). Anyhow, I think most people got quite bored with Him. There was a lot of noise until well after His (and my) bedtime. People sat around (except Him!!) in the tent drinking huge glasses of wine. He'll be whingeing about the cost soon.

Now and then He doesn't have quite so many whiskies. I've linked this to the incidence of flying. He drinks less the day before - I'm wondering why. I bet it's because He's probably unstable before He gets into the poor little thing so that sort of compounds the danger of Him and it falling over. He tells anyone who stands still long enough to have their ear bent that they have written off three helicopters this year at the airfield. According to Him that statistically that decreases His chances of crashing. I bet statistics don't normally have to deal with His kind though.

2nd November

He was quite rude today when He said that the carpets in the house were - and I quote – "pock marked with your pees" - I don't think He should make such personal remarks. It's not my fault - well not always. He fails to leave doors and windows open. Which reminds me, I've discovered, the delights on top of the kitchen table. There's a treasure trove of stuff up there - apples, walnuts (they're good fun, as they scoot all over the kitchen!), crisps, chocolates, and now and then real food. Me and Piglet got into such a state of excitement one day when He was out riding with Kate that I forgot myself and did a 'you know' on the kitchen table. I did panic a bit about that I have to say, but for some unknown reason, He was really quite unmoved by it. Inconsistent as ever.

He told me (and everyone else, which I thought was a bit much) that I had "come of age" today because I was six months old. Heaven knows how He worked that out - I felt and looked much the same as on Monday. Still there you are - no logic, probably no brain. Anyhow, on the strength of that He made me and Piglet follow them on the horses. Actually, I was quite pleased because I longed to see what happened on these long rides. I have to say very little seems to go on except the human failing of practically non-stop chatter. What do they find to talk about?

It seems that at this time of year they get to go on organised hunts for foxes. That means that they have to get the horses fit for the chase so they ride them every day. That sounds quite a gas and I wonder if Piglet and I could form our own pack of rat hunters? It seems that it would be banned, but we could do it undercover. Mole hunting also springs to mind - they wouldn't see us doing that!

3rd November

He's quite fed up today because Piglet and I have discovered how tasty Percy the Parrot's food is. Percy lives in a cage in the kitchen on a table that has a shelf below. On this shelf there are paper bags of parrot food. They stop containing parrot food once you get your teeth into them, and the seed spills out onto the floor in the most amusing way. Then Piglet and I get to hoover it up. I have to admit that there was a tiny bit of a mess when He came back from His silly little helicopter but there was no need for all His noise. He soon calmed down when the Lovely Kate came to pick up Piglet. Anyhow, the house is quiet for the first time for months and He looks completely shattered. He sat and watched television and fell asleep. It was very peaceful I have to admit.

By the way, harking back to what I said earlier – chick crumbs are rather good too. We find them on the veranda on a table that He fondly imagines we can't get onto! I wonder if He ever ponders why the level in the bag goes down rather fast.

4th November

About a foot of water has come up in His larder and the greenhouse was nearly washed away. It hasn't stopped raining for about a week. He plods about in wellies more or less all the time now. He even wears them on the all too frequent visits to His whisky supply in the recesses of the larder. I reckon He'd wear an aqualung if He had to for that errand.

There are some strange and unexplained stirrings in my loins. I am suddenly beginning to feel very peculiar. I'm not at all sure I'm happy about it and it's a bit unnerving. I've had a word with Piglet and he went rather coy and did something slightly unexpected. I haven't decided whether I liked it or not. Is this what He meant about being an adult?

I have got really rather bad tempered and "things" have sort of swelled up. He and Kate are unusually good-natured and Kate whispered in my ear that I am now a woman. I have to admit that that came as a bit of a surprise because until today I had been unaware that I was any different from Piglet. One of the side effects of this is that I get a lot of attention from a motley crew of boy dogs everywhere I go. I am not amused. Even Piglet has slightly changed his attitude towards me. I expect that the whole phenomena can be put down to this vile weather and when things get drier I will go back to normal. Funny that it doesn't seem to affect Piglet in the same way.

5th November

His ex-wife came down to stay with her dog Susie. It taught me to goose (I think that was the term used) the pheasants in the jungle. Great sport I have to say. He says that I may have to be locked up come the shooting season. Whatever for? Surely that is the very time to let me loose on all those stupid birds (N.B. Mr Blair - try stopping a normal red-blooded mammal from hunting. It has to be said that He isn't sure that Mr B has red blood and He says that it certainly isn't blue!).

While on the subject of hunting, I have to say that the kitchen seems to resemble a saddlery more and more with bridles hanging from hook things on the ceiling; saddles on the floor and all manner of uncomfortable other bits and pieces. I'm jolly glad I'm not a horse.

It continues to rain a lot. Did my parents do me a service bringing me to life in this country, and in the countryside? On the whole I think I can just cope with it but it had better stop, soon.

6th November

His elder son Nick came with his girlfriend to stay today together with, horror of horrors, his most peculiar dog (if that is an accurate description) called Hector. Hector's back legs appear to have been something of a bolt-on extra out of the wrong stock pile.   His undershot jaw displays randomly inserted teeth of no uniform size and his whiskers are quite Edwardian.   He's supposed to be a Fox Terrier but I think a fox would make short

Hector

work of him. Mind you he could scare a fox to death just by looking at it. Hector barked a lot for no obvious reason. If it moved, he barked; if it didn't move he barked. Sometimes he just went round in meaningless circles barking. Nick is a big bulky man who merely observed Hector's eccentricities with mild amusement, born of familiarity I suppose. Emma, the girlfriend, was a big strong girl too. She's Scottish so I didn't understand a word she said.

He took us off to the airfield and we were bundled into quite a large helicopter and off we went to lunch with one of his old (and they are getting old) school friends. We sat in the back while He messed about with the controls. For absolutely no reason Hector started barking at things on the ground. He'd stick his peculiarly shaped face out of the little window and grumble at a cow in a field, a man on a bicycle or a bus driving along the road. I suspect it was some form of misplaced snobbery given his very modest background in one of the rougher parts of Edinburgh.

Sam wasn't expecting us so was slightly surprised when we landed on the lawn, interrupting his hedge cutting, and interrupting play in a perfectly happy game of football on the recreation ground next to Sam's house.

7th November

The other son, who seems to be called 'Hurry-up James,' and his wife Anita came to stay the night. He's tall and thin with a bonnet of black hair – He says he looks like an unused safety match. Hurry-up James laughs a lot. No one is quite sure what about and I suspect he's not altogether certain himself. However, in my experience there aren't too many logical reasons for any of them to do anything. There is a funny look about Anita. Rather pot-bellied I would say. He keeps making odd remarks about all sorts of things that in any other house would be regarded as personal but here, as Heather says, seem quite in order. They brought yet another 'lurcher' dog, like Bess next door and just as mad but in a sort of constructive way. It is called Fennel, which I understand is a garden plant.
Are they all obsessed with the land?

8th November

I washed Comatose's eyes again today. They are always so full of sleep. I do wish she wouldn't sleep so much it really is rather hard work trying to keep them clear- actually they are getting quite opaque. Poor old thing. Just so long as I don't have to wash His. I wash her ears too.

Both Nick and Hurry-up James left today taking wives, lovers and, thank God, the lunatic Hector and Fennel with them. Peace at last.

We went for a quiet walk in the woods. I have discovered the delights of reading the messages left on overhanging branches and tufts of grass by other passing dogs. It is fascinating what these smells tell you. He, of course, had to make one of His daft remarks on the subject referring to these places as "Doggy weemail". How silly!

9th November

I rather forgot myself today. One of the baby bantams smelt so good I just had to pick it up to show it to Piglet - it went floppy and we decided that it had rather lost its appeal. He was a bit stuffy about it. Oddly enough, in retrospect, He wasn't half as angry as we expected; positively good-natured. I rather suspect He's hiding something from us. He's too good-natured at the moment. Keeps disappearing for the odd evening and once, a whole weekend! He claimed to be fishing in Devon, but I have an odd feeling that the trout season has finished and He looked pretty worn out when He came back. Kate and Geors looked after us which was really good fun. Two strange young men turned up and there was noise, cigarette smoke, dancing and general jollity. He would have had a coronary if He had seen how much of His wine they all polished off.

He and the Lovely Kate were messing about with horsey things today and an enormous car tore through the village in unseemly haste. Both of them yelled rudely at the driver who turned out to be Vinny Jones. I think that it was a bit of a mistake as I gather V J is pretty big and would deal with them both in no time at all. He went away saying He didn't care who it was and anyway who is this Vinny Jones, which goes to prove just about everything.

10th November

Last night was very unrestful. It rained as if God wanted to have another go at "the flood" and the wind was amazing. Anyhow, we didn't get a lot of sleep for all the banging of doors and windows. Rather like one of those evenings when He has had one or two of His hunting friends in!

They should have gone for an exercise ride on the horses this morning but Kate didn't look too keen and He's in such a compliant mood, they decided to take all of us for a walk to look at all the trees blown down in the park. Actually, it was great fun because we had time to stir up a good few pheasants. Even Comatose broke into a slow trot after one but Bugger Off skulked as usual. Kate ate chocolates and smoked round the woods which would normally have made Him mad but He looked smug. I'm quite worried about Him.

11th November

He's got the flying bug really badly now that He's gone solo a few times – I'm not going in one with Him alone and that's final, not one of those mingy little ones anyway. Which reminds me, He took me to the airfield today. On the way He bought a sandwich but didn't like it and in a vague moment chucked it into the back of the car where He had forgotten I was on duty keeping an eye on things. Well I thought this sandwich was rather good so I dismembered it on the back seat. How was I to know He felt differently about the Mercedes to the Subaru. He screeched to a halt, started picking bits of lettuce, chicken and all sorts out of the upholstery, cursing all the time. I thought He was very grumpy. It was quite like old times.

I have a secret for my journal. Piglet who by any standards is well hung, is having his balls off this week. I have to say the poor boy has trouble with his private parts. Now and then some of them peak out involuntarily. I have an inkling about all this as I had those strange feelings too but so far as I know, I've got nothing needing to be lopped off. I haven't told him because I think he might be a bit upset. Us girls are more sanguine about sex and he'd just go into a decline. He might even run away. Kate and Him were chatting about it, actually they were laughing about it on our walk and I thought it was jolly insensitive of them and quite tacky.

16th November

Ho! Ho! It's happened. Poor Piglet. I have only been allowed to say a brief hello since the dreaded operation because they are worried we'd have those stitches out in no time at all – and they'd probably be right! Piglet said it was a bit sore but on the whole he reckoned that a good rough and tumble would soon make him forget it all!

You won't believe what Kate has done. I watched her – in fact the ghastly act stopped me mopping up one of His horse's breakfast. She told Him that she'd got a present for Him at which point, out of her pocket she presented Him with a small glass jar containing Piglet's balls. I think that was gross. He was ecstatic and there was a lot of excessive giggling. Perhaps the grossest thing of all is that He has put them on the mantelpiece in His sitting room. He said it was to see what Heather would say. I have to say, that the whole episode is pretty tacky and puts both of them in a poor light.

17th November

Today He spent a lot of time trying to get the gravestone sorted out on His wife's grave. He left the back of His car open. I, therefore, escaped and found a pheasant in the churchyard, which I 'goosed'. I also found Barbara (she runs the hotel in the village) who was doing the flowers in the church so I helped her. You know I really don't think 'they' have any taste at all. I rearranged several vases and she was quite stuffy and put them back how they were.

Later, He decided that He needed some pheasants for a meal so He took Comatose (the alleged gun dog) to poach a couple with His air rifle. Give Him His due, He returned with a brace but for some reason He objected to me trying to pluck them for Him. Comatose continued to look vacantly into the distance and I bet she kept falling asleep in the car on the way to and from the wood – all of half a mile.

He claims that He works hard but just to round off the day He went flying again. He missed seeing Kate and was quite gloomy when He got back.

19th November

We're in the grips of yet another storm. I've said it before but I make no apologies for repeating myself. I could have wished for a more equable climate to have been born into. He took us for a very wet and windy walk. I got nose down into one or two very damp molehills - nothing much doing there. I expect they have set off for higher ground. I'm sure the next flood is on its way. Mole hilling is not much fun in this weather.

On the way back across the garden I took a minor detour into one of the flowerbeds to check on the concealment of that really good knucklebone He got us a week or two ago. I had buried it quite well just behind a brand new Lavatera He planted recently. I'm afraid it is beginning to look rather "unplanted" now. I think it's a common, coarse flower anyway. I used the newly disturbed soil to cover my bone but the rain had washed some of it away so I nosed it up again. I don't think He's noticed otherwise He might not be too keen on the condition of His flower and there would be some more yelling.

It was so wet that I had to shake a lot of water out of my coat. I must remember in future not to shake and run. I fell over on the lawn and He laughed! It was very embarrassing and that laugh of His still troubles me.

21st November

When I first got here there were two cats but one disappeared long ago. He said it had gone to a better place in the sky. I hope it keeps a wary eye open for Him in his stupid machine. Anyhow the remaining cat Blot has taken to coming into the house and cuddling up by the Aga with her nose about a millimetre away from the oven door. I don't really mind but I think she should play it by inside rules and not spit coarsely whenever I pass within a foot or so of her.

Anyhow, I'm not sure I approve of the cow eyes she gives Him. He's a pushover for women with those sorts of looks. I'm a lot more subtle. I bit Him yesterday - I didn't mean to, but He disturbed my sleep on the sofa during which I had a mole firmly by the long snout and it was a perfectly natural defensive reaction. He was quite stuffy - I think the fact that I had just eaten what was left of His Galaxy chocolate bar rather niggled Him. He poked my tummy and said He might have to get it back - I was, momentarily, a bit scared so I bit Him again. Sometimes my teeth seem to take charge.

I'm quite amused because Kate has gone off to some wild party with rugby players (or is it the marines this time?) and He has to do the horses and it's still lashing down with rain. All He has to do is walk across the road from the stables and bring in the two geldings while the mare follows on her own, feed them and put their night rugs on. Not a huge undertaking in my view but He makes a lot of noise about it. He makes an even bigger fuss if He has to muck-out the stables but fortunately a local woman who is assumed to be blind and stupid has declared an interest in Him and she keeps tipping up in the village offering to help with the horses, so He has put her to work. She said she liked the disgusting colour of His car, which pleased Him no end. I can't think that that is a good basis for a lifetime of love. Mind you, He hasn't got much of a lifetime left going by the colour of His hair and other tell-tale signs, so maybe He should grab what's on offer when it comes along. I think He'd call that cynical - I call it pragmatic.

22nd November

I redesigned His leather spectacle case today by putting another opening at the opposite end. It's really very useful now because He can put his glasses in from either end and take them out again in the same convenient way. He doesn't seem to see it like that. He was quite crabby about it. Actually, I think He's lost the plot completely. He didn't see me but I watched Him take a packet of cornflakes for a walk across the lawn and back. He took them out of the cupboard in the kitchen and after their outing, He put them back. He'd be locked up in any normal community.

24th November

One of our rituals is to collect the eggs from the hen house, which is right at the end of the garden close to the field. We have become accustomed to surviving the daily storms which are lashing this bit of Dorset so He gets all muffled up in His "rescuing-people-in-the-North-Sea" kit in order to protect His deteriorating body while me, Comatose and Bugger Off have to brave the conditions naked, so to speak. We go for our morning walk then collect the eggs. Comatose has a little lie down to recover from the exertion of the walk and Bugger Off slinks back to the house while I get to go into the hen house through the 'front door' to make sure all is in order and as I like to see it but blow me today, because of the rain, a river has got up in the night and is running full bore through the chicken run. When we got to the gate there was a hen looking disconsolately out of the door at me looking longingly in, but from the other side of the flood. Even He can't be bothered to venture through the rising tide. It's got to stop, all this rain, and I'd like to know who's in charge because I've got one or two things to say on the matter.

30th November

He took Spider hunting to the vale last week. Kate was apprehensive. Sure enough Spider came back with a pronounced limp and He had a bad back. Kate was not amused and, for a change, He slunk about the place keeping His head below the parapet. But Kate was suffering from a hangover and kept below the parapet too, so the place was quite quiet and angst-free for a time.

They are both going hunting tomorrow. Piglet and I are being left here with Belinda in charge. I wonder what we can do. I'm dying to see Piglet's scar. Ho! Ho!. He'll be more aerodynamic now at least - he might even be able to catch me in a straight race. He hasn't the nose for the real stuff of life - viz digging up moles and goosing pheasants!

I've come to the conclusion that Comatose is really almost a normal member of the canine world. She can, for a millisecond or two, seem quite playful. She subsides into doleful somnolence soon after, but there is something of a spark, albeit dull. Bugger Off on the other hand has never shown any sign of playfulness. She's one of those irritating dogs that gets under human's feet all the time, looking soulfully into their eyes and wagging her tail as if to say "Here I am, I'm never naughty like that little rat!" He trips over her and curses.

3rd December

Piglet and I went with them exercising the horses today. They had their 'whizzy knickers' on so it was quite hard work keeping up. We eventually gave up and I gave Piglet lessons in pheasant and squirrel goosing. He hasn't a clue. Much too busy being yobbish. I really do think that since he had that little session with the vet he has begun to be a bit of a brat.

He and the Lovely Kate went shopping for a car for her today. We were put in the back of the Mercedes where He erected the built-in 'dog guard'. Well it took us about ten seconds to find our way round that. I simply can't think how He can imagine that such a puny piece of woven plastic could possibly keep us at bay! Anyhow they settled on a dead smart Peugeot, a lot smarter than the old Subaru He's been lending her but it's white which seems pretty silly in England's muddiest village. What with the following them on the horses, the trip round looking for a car and our inevitable riot in the kitchen when we got back I was exhausted by supper time. I'm rather embarrassed to admit that while He was preparing our meal in the scullery I dozed off leaning against the washing machine. This sent Him into fits of hysterics. I personally can't think that exhaustion is so laughable. I don't laugh when He dozes off at the kitchen table or falls over upstairs when He's been at the whisky. Double standards in my view. Probably double whiskies.

5th December

He took a very beautiful woman out to an art exhibition today. It was an unusually sunny day and He opened the sunshine roof for the first time since well before the flood! This new woman was a brunette and had a lovely lilting voice. Not His usual blonde type but there was the inevitable kissing and so on. I was left in the car, bored, but I greatly enjoyed watching the rain, which suddenly made a comeback, cascade through the open roof onto the two front seats. That'll teach them to leave me in that mouldy old car for hours.

6th December

Piglet is getting a bit big for his boots in Kate's new car. He goes round the place with his nose in the air. He told Kate that much more of that sort of behaviour and she would have to buy Piglet a flat cap, Barbour and four little green wellies. Actually I brought Pig down to earth this afternoon. He has just about mastered the art of cocking his leg. Well he rather forgot that only recently he was slightly redesigned by the vet and therefore his centre of gravity had moved up a bit. He cocked his leg and toppled over! I'm afraid I nearly died laughing. By the way, I was rather scathing about Him taking the cornflakes for a trot across the lawn and back but Comatose has gone one better. She took the wooden bootjack right round the huge wood where we went for a walk today and brought it back again. I think she really has lost the plot this time.

10th December

There have been a couple of pheasants quietly going off in the larder and when the smell had reached delicious proportions He took them out onto the veranda, sat down all muffled up against the cold and with His glasses on He started to pluck them. As far as I was concerned the feathers tasted as good as anything so I took a mouthful into His office. Rather unexpectedly some of them got away from me all over the place. There were some in His desk drawer, where I discovered some chocolate too, some in the keyboard of His computer and a lot behind the photocopier. Heaven knows how they got round so. He didn't see the funny side of it and fooled about with the Dyson. I think that must be something of a first because He obviously hadn't a clue how to use it.

Now that Kate has got her "spangly" (as she puts it) new car I was rather hoping that He would raise His standards a bit so I dug out the old plastic sandwich boxes from the door pockets of His car and sprinkled them round the interior in the hope that He will take the hint. He didn't. I think old age is pretty unattractive. I think His car is a disgrace.

13th December

Great news - Heather has at last noticed Piglet's off-cuts on the mantelpiece in the sitting room. It seems that although she recognised them for what they were right from the start she was too reticent to admit that not only had she seen them but didn't like to say anything as she was not absolutely certain whose they were, and adding that really nothing she found in His house surprised her anymore. I think this made Him think.

14th December

He took all of us for a slightly longer walk than usual today, which I thought might be a bit testing for Comatose. Anyhow we did put up a hare by the new wood and Piglet and I took off after it, as any self-respecting hunting dog would, then low and behold Comatose broke into a run which degenerated into a bit of a shambles when her ill-fitting coat looked as if it might fall right off altogether, at which point she stopped while it readjusted itself round her frame. But it proves that she isn't completely moribund. Bugger Off is quite fleet of foot but hasn't the faintest idea why she is dashing about. She stops eventually, rolls her eyes and returns to her more natural mode of super-skulk.

We bumped into a bizarre old man on a motorized wheelbarrow on a track in the woods. It seems that he is of mid-European extraction and lives on the estate. He has a mound of greying hair, which falls across his face partly obscuring piercing brown eyes. He sports an uncontrolled beard which seem to be all the fashion here and he gets about the place on this curious contraption. Anyhow apparently he is not an illegal immigrant. His living in the material sense is a bit hit and miss. He mends watches which can't be much of a living here as no one keeps to any sort of recognisable timetable and I don't suppose there are that many watches anyway.

17th December

All the horses had new shoes today, which made Him pretty gloomy, and He hid His cheque book. I like the lad (who He says is much too young to know anything about blacksmithing) because he gives us all the hoof parings, which we take into corners of the stables and consume in the luxury of the wood shavings. Now and then I sneak some into the Swamp where they lie undetected for some time and they become seriously rancid, and then Heather gets agitated. I expect she would like some and is upset because we get there first. They make your breath smell absolutely divine. I don't think He agrees but there's no doubt that it's better than the whisky fumes which I have to put up with nightly.

Piglet and I were left on our own for a long time for no obvious reason so we decided to rearrange the lino in the kitchen. It was no time at all before we had taken the bit from under the door and popped it into the Swamp. Then there was a bit by the Aga which we lost in the downstairs loo next to the Swamp along with the bit by the door into the scullery. I quite liked our new arrangements. Anyway He took it all quite badly. For a start He couldn't get into the kitchen for some technical reason to do with the lifting lino and the bottom of the door, which was all beyond me. Then He didn't like to see the very nice concrete by the Aga. Even Kate looked a bit cross, and embarrassed. I really do think they have bizarre taste and worry over the most trivial things.

18th December

Kate is having lessons in how to make Spider a very smart looking horse. He says that it's all totally unnecessary given that all He wants to do is hunt the brute. Anyhow yet another blonde turns up to give these lessons and blow me she brings Dillon, another delinquent Terrier, who turns out to be my (and therefore Piglet's) half brother. Well you can imagine what a wild time we had. Dillon found what was left of a rat which Blot had killed. We had a great tussle and each got bits and pieces of fairly rancid body. By evening all that was left was its enormously long tail attached to a bit of skin. He was not amused when I dragged it into the kitchen. Rather pathetically He picked it up with the fire tongs from the sitting room and heaved it into the bushes. He honestly believes that I don't know where all these tit-bits are. I'll have them under my chair in the sitting room in no time at all. He'll never notice!

25th December

They have this completely bizarre ritual it seems, when on this day every year they eat themselves to a standstill, drink huge quantities of alcohol and give each other presents which they wrap up in all sorts of fancy paper. It seems that it's someone's birthday but even that is a bit obscure. His house also erupted with prickly holly and a good few hundredweight of cards. What amazes me is that most of the cards seem to be from His friends who He sees on a regular basis, if not daily. Can't they say whatever is in the cards in person? There is also a sprig of mistletoe hanging from the light fitting in the hall. This must be the oddest bit of the whole performance. He stops under it wearing that inane grin and every one else especially the women and girls use the back door. He hasn't explained that one to us yet; all part of the ritual I expect. They are all raving mad.

He gave us some leftovers of His lunch and it was reminiscent of pheasant without the feathers. A bit disappointing I thought. One of the horses likes the traditional pudding it seems, so they went through yet another ritual taking some out to the stables. After a bit He subsided onto the sofa and woke up in time to totter off to bed. They really do amaze me.

26th December

He, Kate and His stepdaughter Jemma went hunting as usual and left us here to fend for ourselves. How on earth He managed to rise from the waves of yesterday's overindulgence I will never know. What amazing powers of recovery. I think He looks completely barmy in His red coat and brown top boots. I suppose at least His nose blends in for once. They weren't out for very long. It poured with rain as usual and I expect the contents of His hipflask got rather too watered down so He had to come home to liven it up a bit.

While they were out we found mounds of Christmas wrapping paper, which we redistributed round the house where it looked so jolly . It was enormous fun. Their sudden reappearance rather caught us on the hop and even Piglet looked slightly abashed. I'm sure that they had been at their flasks because all they could do was giggle in a rather juvenile way. Piglet and I went out to help them tidy up the horses and so on. We got into the feed bowls. What fascinating tastes and smells – I think the horses must be French because the have loads of garlic in their feed. I find I quite like it after all.

28th December

A long time ago I discovered what fun the children in the village are. They really look quite like the adults but in miniature and have perfected the art of ignoring anything said to them unconnected with food. They also ignore the 'N' word, so clearly we see the world from about the same stand point. When they fall over it is because they are having a rough and tumble like me and Piglet not because they have been inspecting the bottom of a whisky bottle from the inside. All the children live in the cottages on the other side of the road, which means that I have to run the gauntlet of the traffic – a weekly bus, a few tractors and now and then a resident's car going to or returning from unaccustomed work and Vinny Jones. One of the biggest hazards is His horse lorry, which He parks outside the house ready for hunting. It is such a good place to get under to hide. Sometimes when He thinks that He might be late for the meet and can't get to me He drives off in quite an aggressive way in a pathetic attempt to frighten me into not hiding under vehicles. He must be barmier than I thought. It is such good sport winding Him up like that.

3rd January

Piglet is in serious trouble. It is not often that He gets cross with Pig because He might upset the Lovely Kate, but today His patience was tried too far. I told Pig not to even think about the Waitrose package on the kitchen table but he was too dumb to listen. According to Him it contained a very tasty looking stuffed guinea fowl which He was waxing lyrical about to Kate and how He was going to have it for supper with lovely gravy and so on. I thought at the time that He was making too much of it in front of us, but didn't like to say anything. Sure enough as soon as they went out to do whatever it is that keeps them chirpy Piglet had a good look at it and a sniff and then he had to get up there and fetch it onto the floor where he sampled it just to verify what He had been saying. Then he smacked his lips and somehow there wasn't much left. Just as he got to the last bit he suddenly realised that He might not see it Piglet's way. So guess what, Piglet hid the wrapping paper and what was left of the guinea fowl in Comatose's bed. I have to say that I didn't think that that was very sporting of my brother and told him so.

Sure enough He went orbital when He found that His supper was now irretrievably inside one of us and there was a lot of "I was really looking forward to that" –ing, and Kate looked embarrassed and amused at the same time. It was pretty obvious who had consumed it. Piglet looked for all the world like a small dirigible. I bet if Piglet had had a less pretty owner He would have made a lot more noise! Another reason to get those highlights I guess.

4th February

There is something going on which I only pick up from snatches of giggled conversations between Kate and Jemma after hunting. I was wondering why He was so keen to go hunting with a different hunt, and sure enough there is a blonde involved. From what I can gather she is one of the originals from last Summer. She's tall and has a stunning smile which she uses to great advantage on Him, or so it seems. He goes about the place looking smug and slightly confused at the same time. I expect that she is far too young for Him. Still, in time all will be revealed.

17th February

The whole of life as I have been led to believe it should be lived has stopped because of some frightful disease known as 'Foot and Mouth'. He takes us up the road for our walks now instead of squirreling in the woods. It's terribly boring, the only excitement being when Bugger Off has a go at the Guernsey heifers which are still in the field. She is such a coward. She will only have a go at things if they can't retaliate. She does it to other dogs in cars or on a lead and so on. Talking of which He's completely forgotten about collars and leads and the like. Long may that last

They had their last day of hunting today because of the disease. He and Jemma returned with unbelievable tales of impossibly large jumps at wherever they were hunting. They really do know how to exaggerate. I have to admit that Spider and Fred looked a bit worn out. So did He, but that could be down to just about anything from waking up to driving the lorry followed by a dose of whatever they have at the meet. It's His lifestyle that makes Him tired. Still as He says He will be a long time dead so may as well make the most of being alive.

25th March

He has been shopping and came back with a rather large suitcase. There are piles of clothes all over the place. He brushed His riding hat, which is now on a chair in the kitchen. This all points to Him going somewhere. I am a bit anxious that He might not be taking me with Him. My anxiety has got to my teeth and those led me to the zip on His new suitcase and after a bit of a chew there I had a bit of a go at the leather of His safety harness on His hat. I have to say that that was quite tasty but I didn't tell Him. When He saw the slight muddle on the case He was a bit cross but oh dear I had no idea that the hat was so much loved! What a fuss about such a little blemish. He calmed down after a time and was quite nice to me, which is suspicious in itself. He took to cutting off what remained of the harness so I simply don't understand what all the fuss was about in the first place.

26th March

He is rushing round the house like some demented scarecrow looking for His passport. Now I know He is going away. As it is abroad I'm not going for fear of being "chipped," though who is going to look after me I'd like to know. I don't think He gives enough thought to these important points.

28th March

He went away and left us to the mercy of the two blonde bimbos. Kate kept going off to parties, presumably on the theory of "while the cat's away" and Geors had to take over. I don't like to admit it but I really missed Him, mainly because He knows what food I like and when to administer it. It was the longest He'd been away and as time went on I began to think I'd never see Him again. He tipped up in the middle of the night and I have to say that I very nearly did a 'you know' I was so pleased to see Him. I'm rather ashamed of my display of emotion. In retrospect I think I was a good deal over the top but I don't suppose He noticed. He had been riding round some Middle-East country in the company of four other men and, surprise, surprise, twenty-eight women. He says nothing exciting happened but I'd like to know why He looked so completely clapped out when He got back. And I don't buy the claim that He had a tummy bug and that the flight was long. The phone has been ringing rather a lot. Enough said!

29th March

Slight catastrophe has occurred. The kitchen and all parts between it and the downstairs loo are flooded with faintly horrid smelling water. He calls our dorm the Swamp! This is a real swamp. It seems that a drain is not only blocked but broken as well. The upside of that is that we dogs got to sleep in the dining room and Comatose found that so comfortable that she didn't get up until nearly midday. When Piglet came in at breakfast time we were shut into the dining room and other than the need to duff each other up a bit we found endless new toys and a great game of tag without touching the ground by leaping from chair to chair! A few trashy ornaments got dislodged and He yelled a bit so we took to chewing this and that. I was a little apprehensive about the highlighter pen that Piglet found, but as Piglet said, the chair cover in question was rather a dull red and his electric green highlighter additions do quite cheer it up. I don't think He will quite see it that way. Time will tell.

2nd April

I heard Him on the phone presumably talking to some kind of official. He described himself as self-employed; more like self-unemployed if you ask me. I'm astonished at how little He does in the name of work. Come to think of it there are a lot of men of workable age in this village who don't seem to have any recognisable employment or go anywhere according to a normal working schedule. I don't think any of them are technically unemployed and all seem to be supporting expanding families. Even Bodgit's son has reproduced recently. He says He's not surprised because the chap in question never gets out of bed. I didn't really understand Him. Probably one of His not very funny jokes. There seems to be something of a black economy at weekends though - some of the young men behave quite out of character rushing about the place delivering logs, doing peoples gardens and so on. There always seems to be a building project on the go. The village doesn't get any bigger so I suspect that professional builders have to spend quite a lot of the time sorting out all the disasters left behind by Bodgit and Scarper.

19th April

I am heartily sick of the Foot and Mouth restrictions which force us to plod like geriatrics up and down the lane. When Piglet came to see me this afternoon I took him out onto the lawn and we had a fantastic game of 'chase' through all the flower beds and along the veranda. Bugger Off was out there too and did her best to scold us for being so juvenile so we took to whizzing past her close enough to be able to pretend a quick nip of her skirts. She got very bad tempered and began to skulk in circles grumbling. Kate thought Bugger Off should have "Anger Control" therapy. Then Pig found a nicely smelly something under the oil tanks and brought it out for me to admire so I stole it off him whereupon an even greater chase ensued. Naturally the nice scent of it drifted to Comatose's only active organ. So she had to come out on the principal that if it is edible it's hers; and in some remarkably uncharacteristic bursts of near-energy she tried to relieve us of the trophy. We dodged in and out of her legs. Bugger Off by this time had skulked back to the house. Piglet managed to slow me up by grabbing my tail. I call that a foul.

It has to be said that the idleness enforced by Foot & Mouth has rendered Piglet pretty unfit and he had to have a good few sit downs to puff and pant during all this activity. I kept up the rushing about until He came out to break up the game complaining that we had become a spectator sport and were distracting the staff from their work. Incidentally the object, so He discovered, was a wonderfully rancid rat's head.

10th May

Doris came into our lives today. He came back from flying to find that one of the fourteen bantam eggs that He had been hatching in His new toy, an electric incubator, had hatched. The Lovely Kate gave the poor little thing that name which is fine so long as it is a hen but it won't be too easy to explain if it turns out to be a cockerel. Not much good if you are strutting your stuff in a flowerbed one day with a good looking hen Bantam and she asks your name and you have to reply "Doris". He said, rather gloomily, that it must be the most highly priced ball of yellow fluff in the world if you take into account all the electricity used and the cost of the machine. Miserable old man! If the bad tempered cat doesn't get Doris I will and that will be the end of that!

12th May

Today He went fishing for the first time this season. He has bought Himself a new little fishing waistcoat for the event. He looks quite absurd. The garment has so many pockets He looks exactly like an ambulatory Advent calendar. What's more He has filled all the available pockets with a bewildering array of aids to catching fish. Each time

He opens a pocket some other amazing contraption appears. He really does look a bit like a fishing tackle junkyard. I don't suppose He will be any more successful but He seems inordinately pleased with the thing. Needless to say He didn't catch anything except trees and weeds and added to His repertoire of bad words!

15th May

Comatose is apparently getting very deaf. She hardly hears any instructions that anyone gives her. On our morning walk today she didn't appear to hear Him call her from her bed and so she greeted us at the garden door on our return twenty minutes later as if to say, "If you had said, I'd have loved to come with you." I'm not convinced because she can hear one of His peanuts falling onto the kitchen floor at "top-off-bottle-time" as if an atomic bomb had gone off, and what's more she's as quick as summer lightening getting to the fall zone.

25th May

One of the women that He met on the horse trek in Jordan came to stay today. I wonder why I could have bet good money on her being a pretty blonde and a good deal too young for Him. So it wasn't much of a surprise when He took her and Rachel, one of the wives from the village, flying. It seems that Rachel had to be back at a particular time. She lives in a cottage beside the horses' field in the middle of the village, so He decided to bring her back to her doorstep so to speak. He hadn't reckoned on just about the whole village turning out to watch which rather unnerved Him. The Mayor videoed the event. The field in question is surrounded on two sides by enormous oak trees, on a third by power cables and on the other by our house. He came in over the trees and at the last minute felt that He was rather close to the trees so shimmied a bit to the west, in the process of which it looked as if they might easily land on Rachel's house, so a rather rapid descent took place. He got out sweating. I must say I rather enjoyed the whole thing from the relative safety of a bedroom. The horses were glad to be tucked away in their stables.

16th June

He has completely rearranged his office. It was all quite dramatic. He used to have a big lumbering desk covered randomly with bits of paper. I simply couldn't see how He ever knew where anything was. I suspect that His idea of work is to shuffle the bits of paper around so that it looks like something has happened as new letters surface and old ones disappear. Who on earth writes to Him? Heaven knows. Well, add to all this bits of one of the cars, some parts of some fishing rods, an assortment of umbrellas and a huge butterfly net from a long past enthusiasm littering the room and you will get some idea of the general muddle. He decided that He needed a new desk but couldn't get the old desk out of the door on his own so to my astonishment He took His chainsaw to it, reduced it to three pieces and dumped them outside his office door on the drive beside the road where they remained for a day or two without a single comment from the villagers. Which only reinforces my view that they are all barmy.

He has rearranged the room. His computer is on a purpose built desk and it all looks very smart. I haven't seen Him use it but should He want to it is now much more convenient. He is probably waiting for some work. It might be a long wait but the intention is good.

21st June

He laid on a pantomime for us today. It was all rather fun. Bodgit and Scarper turned up with acres of canvas and ropes and metal poles, steel pegs and other paraphernalia. It was the tent to host another of His parties. Chaos descended on the usually tranquil garden. The bantams went up a tree. Apparently the third member of the Bodgit and Scarper team, the hairy brute from the woods, is indisposed so the two of them attempted to erect the tent. Well they laid it out flat on the ground and then started to poke long poles up it between the sheets so to speak until pegs appeared at three points along the ridge. At this point Scarper got Him, Geors and Kate to stand on the base of each pole. Meantime, Scarper attached some guy ropes to the trellis surrounding the oil tanks and the main ropes were attached to Scarper's car which was parked in the stable yard and Bodgit drove it away in what can only be described as a rather intemperate manner so that the tent rose into the air quite quickly and began a swift descent the other way followed in a graceful arc by the disintegrating trellis thus exposing the oil tanks. Everyone ran in conflicting directions except Scarper who looked on in wonderment and the whole bally thing landed on him. Luckily he could be seen under all the canvas ferreting about in a demented sort of way eventually emerging quite ruffled and red. The process was repeated later but in a rather more dignified manner and the tent started to rise from the ground without the drama. Bodgit, who seemed quite unconcerned anyway, started to beat steel tent pegs into the lawn with a lump hammer until he hit something solid. He got agitated at that point realising that the pin in question was trying to penetrate the main sewer drainpipe that ran down the lawn. Scratching his beard Bodgit began to tie ropes to anything he regarded as solid enough to take the weight of the quite big tent. At about this point He retired to the sanctuary of the kitchen to watch from a safer distance.

I must admit that I am not at all sure that this has not been just a dress rehearsal for the real cabaret tomorrow night and that by then Bodgit & Scarper will have perfected their act so that something really significant will be catapulted over the stable block for the amusement of the guests. Anyhow eventually it all got put up and only one side fell down, which was then propped up again with some hazel poles out of the woods.

22nd June

Sixty or more people turned up. Some are staying here, and I am not amused. The jollity started at about "top-off-bottle-time" and went on until some frightful time in the morning. Kate arrived. He had never seen her all smartened up for a party and it nearly killed Him. I am sure I saw steam come out of His ears. The now very regular Emma was there too, which made Him look even odder. It was very noisy and I got very little sleep. Comatose came out to see what all the excitement was, gave a token bark and retired to her bed for two days. Bugger Off skulked about and finally went to ground in His office. Everywhere there were people; one even went to asleep on His bathroom floor where I can usually find peace and quiet in the armchair if all else fails. I eventually found an abandoned plate of food in the sitting room tucked into it and retired under my chair.

23rd June

I kept falling asleep today and He laughed in that gruesome manner of His. All the guests were gone by lunchtime. He went round telling them that it was time they went home which was quite rude but I had to agree with Him He complained endlessly about a painful back, which in my opinion was a self inflicted wound caused by trying to dance with people half His age in a thoroughly embarrassing way. He decided that if He stretched His back by hanging from a hook in a beam in the kitchen, it might help his ailment. So He did and it gave way, and He fell onto the floor hitting His head on Percy's table and damaging His hip on the floor. I don't suppose the stars He saw were any different from a normal morning after but He could hardly walk for a week. Dotty old thing!

10th July

Dillon's owner has got a baby girl. I cannot see the point. It doesn't do anything. It doesn't move visibly. It doesn't say anything. It waved a rather podgy arm for a brief moment and went back to sleep. A bit like Comatose really. Kate and Him drooled over it in some undignified ritual. They poked it and made funny noises. It should have bitten them. It doesn't have any hair. I have seen better-looking baby mice, and I expect they taste better too. As far as I can see there are far too many people around here already so I can't understand why on earth they go out and get more. Of course it might have been on special offer at Waitrose. They will buy anything if it is on special offer. They needn't bring it around here again until it can at least articulate its body, if not its voice.

20th July

Disaster! Having reequipped His office with expensive electronics which buzz and whirr He did start to use His computer, and even surprised Geors by sending her an email from time to time. Well, Kate was looking after an uncoordinated Labrador puppy called Toad for the weekend while his owners were away. Virtually no part of Toad's wayward body seems to be attached particularly well to any other part so that the whole was a shambles. I suppose that Comatose was like that once. I am not sure which condition I prefer; the nearly dead or the barely assembled. Anyhow, on this occasion the three of us were having a bit of a tussle over a bone which had avoided 'the purge' in His office when Toad got tangled up in the cables of the printer. Fearing that this was one of us attacking from behind him he took off attached to the printer, which shot across the room and into the fireplace with a terrific crash. It wouldn't have mattered half so much if HE hadn't been working at His computer at the time!!! I have to say that I have never heard Him bellow like that before. Piglet and Toad retired very swiftly to the kitchen and I crawled under His plan chest and hid behind an ancient typewriter which belonged to His Father so must be a museum piece in itself. I believe that the printer is broken. I am not too keen to find out and I am going to keep a very low profile indeed for some time.

It's funny how these disasters happen all at once. I can go for days without Him feeling the need to yell then, like summer moles after a drought, we have a spate of little problems. It wasn't long after the 'printer incident' that we had the unpopular redesigning of the plastic stopper from His vacuum flask. I have to admit that none of us can remember how it got out of the flask, nor who actually did do the job but He was not pleased. Although the weekend was rather fun there were moments when Toad's presence was a bit disruptive. I am quite glad that he is not a permanent member of the gang.

18th August

I went into hospital on Friday. I had the most appalling tummy ache and had felt pretty dreadful all day. I felt so miserable that I had to hide away in my little secret places like under my chair in the sitting room and under His plan chest in the office. He kept finding me and was nice, but to be truthful all I wanted was to be alone. Piglet came to see me in the afternoon. He started to fool about and be laddish so I bit him. I really couldn't be doing with all that. I have to admit that He was very attentive and kind but my tummy did hurt.

Anyhow when we got to the veterinary clinic the vet poked and prodded me so I bit him too and he didn't do it again but instead he stuck something up my bottom which I did not think was at all funny. It was a most peculiar sensation! The upshot of all this was that they think that I have something stuck in my tummy, probably from when I fell into the river yesterday and got swept over the weir while He was fishing further upstream. He had pulled me out of the water cursing and saying that I looked like a drowned rat. I can remember taking in huge gulps of water, but not the stones that they rather think are inside me now!

As you can imagine He has used the whole episode as an excuse for one of His pathetic jokes at my expense. He says that I am probably harbouring one of His trout, so now it is a fish within a Fish and no wonder He can't catch anything if I keep eating them direct from the river. Frankly, with a tummy as sore as mine is, I don't think any jokes are in very good taste.

Today is my second day in Hospital. He came visiting and was quite soppy. I am afraid I couldn't hold back and allowed the smile to return to my bottom, as He puts it. I feel better and the nurses are really nice. One of them is Kate's sister but as soon as I got here she went off duty. I don't see the point of having friends in low places if that is their behaviour just when I need them.

11th August

I am back home and ready for all the little comforts like His bed, the Aga, my secret place under the chair and best of all beating-up Piglet to pay him back for his oafishness on Friday. On our walk today He took a good deal too much notice of my bowels, which I thought very intrusive. He laughed in that silly way of His and said that He was waiting for His trout. Not very funny.

26th August

He decided to take us all on another trek in the New Forest today. It wasn't too much of a surprise that He stopped off to collect the now rather regular visitor Emma and her two dogs. He said that He felt like a dog warden with a van full of strays. I didn't think that that was very polite. We went in the Subaru in an attempt at un-impressing the bird I suppose, or maybe to preserve the interior of the Mercedes but in that case I reckon that is too little too late. Actually I rather like it as they have very considerately provided a nice place for me to perch on the parcel shelf of the dashboard. I must say that car manufacturers are good the way that they cater for me in this way. He of course has to have His pathetic joke about "Fish Perches". I don't suppose that I would laugh even if I knew what He found so funny. His sense of humour is a bit obscure.

We went miles along paths and through purple heather. It was quite energetic so I expect she had to hold His hand to stop Him falling over. He eventually stopped under an enormous beech tree where He picked some white heather for Her. It was supposed to be romantic I expect but seemed a long way to trek for a tiny sprig of something that He could have got for pence in Salisbury market any old Tuesday.

10th September

Doris has started to crow in the early morning and quite often during the day too. Whoops!

16th September

He really did take me to a foreign country today. He piled up the car with all manner of junk including four guns and ten (yes TEN) fishing rods, endless clothes, suitcases and to my eternal horror Bugger Off and Comatose. The faint whiff of my food hidden under the floor in a secret compartment was slightly comforting. Anyhow He drove with a manic will straight up this country and, after what seemed like days, we fetched up in a very bumpy country where everyone spoke a sort of patois, which I found completely incomprehensible. They looked rather hairy too and believe it or not the men wear skirts. God help us all if He starts that sort of thing. I believe we are in Scotland

The house where we ended up is big and imposing. He went up to the front door rang the bell and walked in. I thought that was quite impolite of Him. Who knows what the owners must have thought by His casual manner. Anyhow I decided that I'd better introduce myself too so I insinuated myself past Him into this enormous hall all decked out with the sharp ends of very big Red Deer, who had apparently failed to get all their bodies in through the walls so had contented themselves with just their head and necks. Very odd. At this point an incomprehensible woman started shooing me out. It seems that Dogs aren't allowed in this house. What sort of country is this? I'm not going to like it here. He can take me home whenever He likes.

17th September

It was extremely cold sleeping in the car. I did not appreciate being cooped up with Bugger Off who smells less delectable every day, especially in the car. Comatose snored all night. The atmosphere was foetid by the morning. I gave Him one of my most gimlet eye looks when He deigned to arise from His stately bed.

It got better after that. The driveway had suddenly sprouted lots more cars during the night and six more dogs of varying sizes and breeds. His son Nick has brought his peculiar dog Hector who is still running round in circles barking at nothing in particular and his back legs haven't got any better. There were a few more faces that I recognised;

ex-wife's funny little dog called Susie, Hurry-up James's big lurcher and Step-son Nick's barmy Flatcoat Retriever. There were some more but not noteworthy. They didn't join in the killing game.

They all assembled their rods and disappeared in the direction of what I later found to be a raging torrent of a river.

19th September

He went walking up the enormous hill near the house today. I have never seen Him in such a state of collapse (other than when the whisky bottle needs to be emptied!) when He returned empty-handed. Bulky son Nick had to help Him down the hill. He made such a fuss. Had to have a bath with a whisky beside the tub and someone to wash His back and massage the sore bits. Had to have some special restorative wine (so He said but I'm not sure that He was telling the truth), and after dinner had to tell endless stories of the rigors of the "stalk" and finally drifted off into a deep sleep on a sofa.

20th September

He went fishing and took us dogs with Him. Bugger Off hasn't the faintest idea why we are here. I'm not altogether surprised since no one has managed to kill anything at all but you would have thought that all the paraphernalia they have brought like guns and fishing rods might have given the crabby old thing a faint clue. Comatose isn't too keen on all this fresh air and activity. Sometimes she sits down amongst the bracken and heather just in eyeshot of Him and dozes off in the sunshine. He leaps from rock to shingle changing flies and cursing just about everything for tangling His line or snagging it on trees, fences and His own clothes. He had to just about undress to get the hook out of His shirt collar. After that the salmon stopped jumping, which made Him mad. I suspect they had glimpsed His body and it put them off for a time.

There was a good deal of excitement at one point. He decided that His "ex" should take a photograph of Him, the intrepid hunter, standing in the middle of the raging torrent in His waders and so on but He thought it might add a certain cachet to the pose (and I had to agree with Him) if He had his faithful terrier by His side. I was on the other bank of the river so He called me over. At first I wasn't too keen as there was a stretch of raging torrent between us. The water looked itchy and rather manic but the fearless terrier in me came out and I plunged in. Well there were currents all over the place which tugged at my skirts and try as I did the only direction that I seemed to achieve was down! Then I bobbed up and down a good few times and He got agitated. Probably not half as agitated as me actually. He plunged in, abandoning His rod, swam to me, grabbed me and pulled me under with Him. I had hoped that His intention was to rescue me but in the event it seems that He was just making sure that I drowned. After a while we struggled to the bank where He displayed a lot of quite unnecessary emotion and used soppy language on me. We trudged off to the house so that He could change and recount to any poor soul who was unlucky enough to get caught by Him about His heroism. Quite an eventful day I suppose.

22nd September

Apparently it is His eldest son's birthday today. Two of the young people went off after stags and the rest fooled about by the river. The predictable party got underway as soon as He took the lid off the whisky that evening. There was a lot of jollity and merriment. And the inevitable happened. He took up 'carpet sliding' in the hall with one of the young girls. During this undignified activity He fell over and cracked His head on the parquet floor with such a bang the whole glen shook. He was more than usually insensible for quite a time and people who didn't know Him well looked concerned. He was unusually quiet. Actually it must have been quite bad because He didn't drink any alcohol for two days. That in itself must have been shock enough to His system to nearly kill Him.

24th September

We left Scotland today. There were lots of farewells and kissing. Hurry-up James kept up a monologue of whittering and laughing at nothing in particular which is just a little reminiscent of Him. As soon as we got back to Dorset I did two circuits of the village to re-establish contact with my friends, the children and the vermin and I have to say it's good to be by the Aga again! The bantams were very welcoming too as they rushed round the lawn squawking while I attempted to tell them about the adventure.

Scotland is OK but it's too busy for Comatose, incomprehensible to Bugger Off and not good for Him. He seemed rather too pleased to be back home with Emma. I didn't see Him for what seemed like days and the celebratory bottle of single malt didn't last long! They talked a lot about a party and marquees and so on. Another sleepless night I suppose.

11th October

I feel rather peculiar again. He keeps looking at me oddly and discusses pretty private things with Kate referring to me I think. I get a lot of attention from the other dogs in the village. I even have to fight off my half-witted brother sometimes. It is all quite irritating and I hope I recover soon so that my life can go back to normal.

18th October

There was a funny glint in His eye today. He bundled me into the car and not long afterwards we found ourselves at this horrendous place lifting with other members of my tribe. I was deposited in a gruesome cage and a rather over friendly boy dog was insinuated. I realised that this was an attempt at a honeymoon. What a performance. He left me there all day. I spent my time nipping round the bridal suite avoiding the chap. He was nice enough but I wasn't in the mood.

It was good to get home in the evening. Comatose woke up long enough to sniff me in a rather personal way as if to say "Oh you've been there have you?" before drifting off again.

21st October

Everyone got up really early today as there was a cubbing meet here on the estate. Normally He's away most of the day but He was back in no time at all handing the big black brute of a horse to Kate. He put me back into the car and off we went again to what He has begun to refer to as my "nooky factory".

I was not as cross as I thought I was going to be. They introduced a new bridegroom to me and if the truth is known I really took quite a fancy to him. Of course He had to have a celebratory whisky though I thought it was in poor taste to celebrate such a personal event. He took to chuckling which is just better than His frightful laugh.

18th November

I have been feeling quite odd the past couple of weeks. My appetite has increased and my tummy is getting fatter but at a disproportionate rate to my rate of food consumption. Anyway He took me to the surgery and all the nurses crowded round me while the vet took video pictures of my insides. It seems that I am going to have at least two puppies. He of course got soppy again and cooed into my ear so I bit Him. He was rather cross but I hate it when He gets sentimental.

22nd November

Bugger Off didn't look too good last night. She came into the swamp and lay down. He came in too and said nice things to her which was in itself notable. This morning she died. He and Kate buried her in the garden under the cherry tree. I will miss her if only for the perfection of her art of skulking.

15th December

It is getting very tricky going for walks in the woods. My undercarriage keeps getting caught on twigs, molehills and so on. Sometimes I think my babies are practising molehilling in my tummy. It is quite an odd feeling and I'm not sure I like it. One good thing about being pregnant is that He is very attentive and my food is obviously shipped in from The Savoy Grill.

He has made a huge wooden dog bed and nothing has fallen off it yet which is just about a first for His carpentry. He has put it in the swamp and filled it with nice old coats, blankets and one of His scarves and best of all one of Geor's duvets. I think He wants me to have my puppies in the bed. I think I will decide where that event will occur.

21st December

Well it happened last night and in the new bed in the swamp. I had three boys. He sat up with me and fussed about, irritating me, until I had had enough and bit Him. He went to bed then so that I could do my housekeeping in peace. I have to say that my boys are a good deal prettier than Karen's baby and smell a lot nicer. They make funny little squeaky noises a bit like some of my childhood toys. Quite promising I think.

26th December

I have had a procession of villagers day and night to admire my babies and practically no one ever stops to mention my bit in all this. To be fair He does from time to time remind them but on the whole I might as well not exist. It rather irritates me and I take it out on the poor little mites. You will never believe what He has named them. Well the rather sweet little one who was born last is called Maggot, the brown and white one Worm and the big butch boy Grub.

A family of four came in this afternoon bringing with them their uncontrolled lurcher puppy who took up bantam chasing. Poor Blondie got up such a head of steam flying away from the dog down the lawn that she forgot to stop at the veranda and flew straight through the kitchen window and landed on the floor amid a shower of glass. It didn't seem to phase her much. She blinked a few times, tottered off stage right and back through the door into the garden He seemed completely undisturbed. Sometimes I think He is just about dead.

27th December

Poor Comatose died today. I am not sure that she would have been able to put up with the Hooligans so after a long and uneventful life she's sleeping somewhere else now. I've got my hands full for the time being but I know that I will miss her and her sleepy eyes. At least life was quite peaceful with just her, Him and no hooligans.

18th February

He is not hunting much at the moment because one of His horses is losing her eyesight which rather adds to the inherent dangers of the pursuit given His natural instability and all the other hazards. Therefore He has been concentrating on hunting the black brute, which, due to His over exuberance one day with the Wilton round some of Mary Gordon-Watson's cross country course, has done a tendon. Therefore now He has to do some unaccustomed office work. It will help with the housekeeping bills for the Hooligans I suppose. We take them for walks into the woods and they are getting the hang of molehilling, cocking of their legs and not doing you knows in the swamp which does rather resemble that sort of terrain now and then. They have dug a neat hole in His lawn and the whole place is littered with plastic flower pots, bones and squeaky toys. Very juvenile

1st March

He has started taking us all about with Him in the car. After a few worrying moments fending off the little Hooligans, who seem to behave unbelievably badly in the car, He finally bought a dog guard in order to pen them in the back.

7th March

He has installed a stair gate to prevent the Hooligans going upstairs. Needless to say it doesn't do the job very well and they have discovered how to get through it. When will He learn that to a Jack Russell terrier all obstacles to movement have to be overcome somehow or other. Anyway today they got through it little realising He was in His office doing some unaccustomed work and they went for a hooley, apparently in their wellies, along the passage above His head. Bit of a give-away. He ran out into the hall and yelled at them. They appeared at the top of the stairs looking guilty and tumbled down in truly shambolic puppy fashion. He yelled again so Grub legged it to His office and onto the top of His desk. He rushed in, still rather vocal, at which point Grub peed on a bill from Wessex water. He didn't seem to mind. I will never fathom out His mental processes.

14th March

Maggot has gone to live with Karen and her family. They have moved into the village so that Karen's husband, Roger, can brush up on doing not very much like all the rest of the men here. It is a bit more peaceful without Maggot but I have to admit that he was the only one of the three that I less frequently thought of murdering. They have re-christened the poor little thing Norman! That says just about all there is to say about humans I should have thought. I see a lot of him still because Karen and the silent baby come round quite often to help with the horses. Two blondes in the stables. He'll have a stroke and that will be that.

15th March

He went shopping at Waitrose again today and we all went with Him. He was away quite a long time. Worm and Grub began to riot a bit so I admonished them. They settled down for a short time in the far back of the car behind the guard. It was too quiet. I went to see what was happening only to discover that they were sinking their little teeth into the new dog guard in no uncertain terms in an attempt, no doubt, to get back to the front.

Well I told them that I thought He would be pretty cross about the episode as the guard was expensive and anyhow I simply couldn't understand why they had to chew everything!

Worm

Grub

Me

END